Playing with Posture

Positive Child Development using the Alexander Technique

Sue Holladay

First published in 2012 by HITE
HITE Limited, 10 Harley Street, London W1G 9PF
Email: info@hiteltd.co.uk
Website: www.hiteltd.co.uk

A CIP catalogue for this book is available from
the British Library.

Book and cover design by Nalini Thapen
Printed and bound by CPI Group (UK) Ltd, Croydon, CR0 4YY

ISBN: 978-0-9568997-1-2

Note to Readers

This book conveys the opinions and ideas of its author. It is sold with the understanding that neither the author nor the publisher are providing medical advice. If the reader has any concerns, or requires advice, a doctor should be consulted.

The ideas and games outlined in this book may not be suitable for everyone, and are not guaranteed to produce any particular results. The reader will gain most benefit from reading alongside having lessons with a qualified Alexander Technique teacher.

Both the author and publisher specifically disclaim any responsibility for any liability, loss or risk, personal or otherwise, which is incurred as a consequence, directly or indirectly, of use and application of any of the contents of this book.

Some names and identifying details of the individuals mentioned in this book have been changed to protect their privacy.

If you would like to contact the author or publisher with any comments, requests, or suggestions, then please email: info@hiteltd.co.uk

To my three children, Oliver, Nicholas, Lucilla,
and six grandchildren,
who have led me along this delightful and rewarding path of learning,
with my love and thanks.

Contents

Foreword

Sue brings to this work the same quality of lightness of being, playfulness and delight that I experienced from her teaching when I began my own journey with the Technique some 12 years ago. My first encounter with the Alexander Technique had been through musicians describing the greater ease with which they created sound. As a violinist (albeit amateur), I was intrigued. Subsequently, in my role as a chiropractor, I questioned the use of external functional appliances to 'correct' or optimize the mechanics of the foot and temporo-mandibular joints, and I began taking lessons myself.

With this experience I recall observing that primary school children would benefit if the teaching of the Technique were part of their formal learning experience. Over the years this instinct has been borne out as I have observed the benefits in children of all ages who have taken lessons. There are, of course, the direct and more tangible benefits of effortlessly making a fuller sound when playing a musical instrument, or improvements in co-ordination. More profoundly, the ease within the body that they develop seems to help these individuals navigate the challenges of transitional periods in their lives, or what we might call 'rites of passage', like puberty.

However 'Playing with Posture' has a far broader scope. The book excels at communicating the essence of the Alexander Technique in such a way that is very readable and also highly kinaesthetic – immediately I read the directions ...

'Let the neck be free
To let the head go forward-and-up,
To let the back, lengthen and widen,
And let the knees go forward-and-away'

... I feel my body responding! Head forward and up, back opening and I notice that I carry this reawakened awareness with me in all the normal comings and goings that make up my day. What a joyful, peaceful and delightful space this is! It's a place from which there is space to chose my perspective in any given moment. I particularly like Sue's short form, 'Stop, Think, Act', as I feel it's a useful translation of the directions both for those who have not yet had the experience of one-to-one Alexander Technique lessons and for those who have. It shortens the directions to a form that both children and adults can very easily integrate into their lives making all the benefits of being truly present in one's body, and therefore present in all activities, accessible in a new way.

When I recommend patients take Alexander Technique lessons it can be a challenge to convey the essence and therefore value of the Alexander Technique in a way that makes the potential benefits meaningful to an individual. This book easily and clearly communicates this message by demonstrating its applicability to the everyday, through examples of activities and tasks that most people can relate to, such as pushing a supermarket trolley, sitting at a desk or washing-up. The inclusion of games for parents and teachers to play with children provides ample opportunities for practical exploration and fun.

The author brings to this work the unique combination of the authority of a teacher who has a wealth of experience in many different contexts and a compassionate understanding of the 'human condition' - our lapses, our forgetfulness as we fall into old patterns of postural strain and compromise. The material is readable and accessible through the sharing of personal experience and the lightness of approach. Those 'slouching' postural tendencies are explained when we understand that too much tension in one muscle group pulls us into a place of compromise. As we comprehend the roots to such patterns we can let go of the idea that it is about laziness – and then there is room for a different choice, beginning with freeing the neck, – breakthrough!

Neuro-developmental delay and the remediation of persistent primitive reflexes is an area of special interest in my work with children. Sally Goddard-Blyth has been profoundly important to the area as a whole and to my personal practice and references to her work within this book give further validation to 'Playing with Posture'. I have observed some of the most rewarding and dramatic results as the retained reflexes are inhibited, allowing age appropriate neurological development to be restored and completed. It is an area of work that is huge in terms of positive consequences for the individuals enabling them to reach their full potential. It is also an area which, despite compelling evidence, continues to be largely neglected at huge cost to individuals and their families with the consequent implications for society as a whole. It is particularly gratifying that this topic is covered in a straight forward and encouraging manner in this book and in such a way that the material will be relevant to parents, teachers, both mainstream and special needs, and to the wider field of health practitioners.

'Playing with Posture' is relevant to the individual who wishes to gain an initial understanding of the Alexander Technique, perhaps before embarking on lessons, and for different reasons would be equally helpful for those already having lessons. It is highly relevant for parents and carers of children and its scope is sufficiently broad to be a manual for parenting. Sue's commonsense style is refreshing and her message is ultimately uplifting and inspiring.

Alison Edwards
Chiropractor
Cambridge, England

1. Introduction

'We don't stop playing because we grow old; we grow old because we stop playing' George Bernard Shaw – Playwright and pupil of FM Alexander

Searching for ideal posture

I often encounter people, who, when they learn that I teach the Alexander Technique, immediately straighten up with an apologetic smile, referring to their bad posture. Guilt registers in every gesture, as if they assume that it is simply laziness that stops them from maintaining good posture at all times. However, they are unable to continue holding this postural stance for more than a few minutes before they relax again into the other, more familiar position – their habitual stance.

Where does this guilt come from? Partly from the vague sense we have of something precious lost – a sense of ease and lightness that we vaguely remember from early childhood; partly from specialist advisors who see that undue muscular pressure on the body leads to pain, stiffness, and lack of flexibility. We feel somehow that we should not have thrown away so carelessly the childhood inheritance of balanced and fluid functioning that we took for granted until it was too late to retrieve it again.

Ideals of posture continue to be influenced by social norms and political affairs. I have an anatomy book compiled from the works of BS Albinus whose copper plate engravings of 1747 were discovered in the 1970s.[1] Apart from the great beauty of the finely wrought backgrounds, the engravings are remarkable for the beauty of the human form displayed, which is in an artistic pose, and demonstrates an ideal of posture as released rather than toned, fluid rather than drilled.

The social norms of the 18th century were more aligned with grace and artistry than with postural discipline or with muscular strength. In the last century, the assumption was that the army should set the postural standard for human beings: head up, shoulders back, chest out and ... quick march. Nowadays, the social ideal of keeping fit has affected people's posture, setting a new standard of strongly toned muscles around arms and shoulders, with strong legs, coupled with a relaxed slouch when not working out.

Posture is conditioned by habitual movement

Why don't human beings, born into the gravitational field and developing their movement patterns as their brains mature, again within the gravitational field, have perfect movement and therefore, perfect posture?

In my opinion, there are three key reasons why we don't all have perfect posture – reactions to stress, imitation of others and inherited conditions. We cannot change our inherited condition but we can look at how we react to situations and copy those around us.

Our reactions to early stress are related to the way we register emotion: totally instinctively, but often without understanding or awareness. A baby who has repeated unpleasant or frightening experiences, like parents shouting at each other, may not understand the place of those experiences in the overall scheme of things, and shrinks from contact with the person or environment that appears to cause these unpleasant experiences. This constant flinching may become incorporated into habitual reactions and form part of that individual's experience of reality and relationships.

Imagine that your infant attends a nursery where another child grabs the toys out of his hand or pushes him off the ride-on car. The staff may feel that this is a learning situation that your child will learn to handle in time. Then you notice that your child doesn't want to go to the nursery any more, yet he has to go and you have to get to work. Eventually he gets used to it, and seems to be doing well after the minor hiccup and you relax.

But his learning has taught him to avoid, or maybe to match, the aggressive child's behaviour. He has learned a defensive pattern which he will use in anticipation of threatening behaviour, no matter what the circumstances. If these experiences are repeated over time, he will remain, just to be sure, in his defensive state habitually, tensing muscles that are normally used in emergency situations. This can continue through life, causing a limitation on the freedom of his movement.

When your learned responses make you repeat the same movements over and over again, your brain and muscles connive to produce a unique pattern that is your very own and shapes your body and your posture. Wilhelm Reich referred to this as 'body armouring' where the human being armours himself muscularly against psychological hurt.[2] These defences can be observed in a person's way of talking, walking and moving.

Why the Alexander Technique is unusual

In the normal run of things, when you learn a skill, such as singing, your coach will instruct you to carry out certain physical actions, such as taking a breath to be ready for the phrase, and looking up and out while you sing. You will interpret these instructions according to your very own brand of body armouring, and try as best you can to carry them out within the confines of your habitual stance. For example, if you have a habitual stoop, you will try and overcome this stoop by lifting your chest to look out rather than down. The stoop remains fundamentally unchanged, as it is part of your normal state, and this interference means that you have to add more tension in your back to hold the new position. The result gives you only partial success at taking a breath and looking out. The voice cannot be really free.

In learning the Alexander Technique, your teacher will show you how to keep yourself free from interference and tension, and focus on avoiding any unnecessary movements; so that your in-breath can arrive in the lungs with the least restriction and the greatest speed, and your head remains balanced and free when you are looking up and out, thus leaving your voice open and unimpaired.

Any activity you choose can take place with minimum interference and maximum efficiency once you understand the principle of staying balanced, and then making only the appropriate amount of effort to achieve your aim.

Education and positive child development

'Only the educated are free' Epictetus – Greek philosopher

It is widely acknowledged that education of the young is the best method to improve life and living standards. Having money for material comforts and leisure in which to enjoy them, come second in many people's value system to acquiring a good education. With education, problems can be more intelligently addressed and adaptability of the mind is enhanced. The educated person is expected to have more poise and command over himself and his life.

One would expect educated minds to cope more easily with the increased demands of modern living. What one sees instead, however, are minds that, though fearsomely intelligent, are encased in bodies that are barely able to function due to excessive levels of tension.

The instincts that human beings rely on for coping with the demands of modern living are often poorly adapted and inappropriate, formed as they were in prehistoric times when survival was of the most basic physical kind and instincts were either to freeze or to run away. It is simply not appropriate to draw up your knees, close your eyes and protect your head when driving into a car crash. Much better to keep your eyes open and apply the brakes.

Without self awareness and understanding we are disadvantaged. Our instinctive habits no longer serve our needs. True freedom to respond appropriately as needed comes through good physical and emotional skills, recognising that they are totally interlinked, and which ideally need to be taught in childhood.

Better psycho-physical skills can easily be taught to children, who have not had time to lose their natural grace and symmetry. These skills will form a more reliable foundation for learning and life through childhood and schooling.

Balance is the quality most needed and often most lacking, particularly in the intellectual person, whose energy has been over directed towards improving the mind at the expense of the body. The defensive postures seen widely, of jutting the chin forward, raising the shoulders, hunching the back are more appropriate to the animal world, where size, strength and territory ensure survival. Yet if you annoy another motorist by getting in their way, you are likely to be treated to an aggressive display of strength in just the way I have described. For a sophisticated, speedy culture, this surely is inappropriate behaviour.

Let us instead look at how we can teach our children to manage their bodies, their posture, their reactions to stress and conflict, and allow themselves to adapt quickly and easily to the increasingly demanding pace of change likely in their lives and that of their children - your grandchildren. For this to happen, it may surprise you that you will need to start with thinking about yourself.

You will see in the following pages that the essential component of good postural management depends on cultivating a freely organised, balanced, adaptable relationship between the head, the neck and the back. 'The head leads and the body follows' is a phrase that runs throughout. For that to happen appropriately, your children need to become aware of their heads and what they tend to do – their habits – with their neck and shoulder muscles. And for that to happen, they need to be taught to stop, to think, before plunging into action.

The theme of this book is about how, through managing the body's posture and maintaining its freedom you can help your child get ahead in life. By playing with posture, I would like to show you how you can have a positive impact on your child's development using the Alexander Technique.

Can the Alexander Technique help your child

'I wish I had known about Alexander when my children were children!'
Alexander Technique pupil

If your child:

- Needs 'Mens sana in corpore sano' – a sound mind in a sound body
- Is interested in sport
- Wants to or is learning a musical instrument
- Often complains of back, shoulder or neck pains, or gets tension headaches
- Has poor posture and often seems slumped and unable to sit up straight for any length of time, for example while working at a desk
- Tends to have the head poked forward habitually rather than it being balanced on top of the spine
- Has pain or burning in arms, wrists or hands. Spends a lot of time at the computer or phone, playing games, messaging or texting
- Frequently becomes angry or frustrated
- Often becomes anxious and stressed
- Finds it hard to relax and has difficulty sleeping
- Finds it hard to write neatly, or uses a lot of tension while writing
- Is self-conscious about his or her body or is clumsy in movement
- Has poor co-ordination

Then ... this book is very relevant for your child.

However, start with yourself! Having checked the list to see which of the above relates to your child, check it again to see which ones relate to you.

If any apply to you, then it will help your child immensely for you to learn the Alexander Technique for yourself. As I said earlier, one of the key reasons why we don't all have perfect posture is because behaviour is learnt largely through imitation. Children unconsciously mimic the behaviour including posture, of those closest to them. By setting them a good example you will stand them in excellent stead.

The Alexander Technique is a conscious learning process and this book will help you understand more about it. It can be taught to children, so the format and teaching method needs to be adapted to the age of the child. You, as parent or guardian, are the child's primary teacher. He learns everything about life from you.

In this book I explain how playing with posture using the Alexander Technique can make learning about life as positive an experience as possible.

You might prefer to read this book straight through or you may like to just dip into sections that interest you or seem most relevant to your child. I would recommend that you have a go at the 'Reset and Restore' lying down exercise in Chapter 6 as you can apply this straight away. The appendix has a comprehensive set of games that you can explore with your child.

2. Foundations

'There is only one corner of the universe you can be certain of improving, and that's your own self' Aldous Huxley - Author and pupil of FM Alexander

Alexander Technique origins and now

The Alexander Technique is named after Frederick Matthias Alexander (1869–1955) who was born in Tasmania. He was a weak and sickly child and was partly educated at home. One of his tutors imparted a great love of English literature and of reciting Shakespeare. His dream was to become a professional actor and reciter. He moved to Melbourne to further his career and spent all of his spare time studying to achieve his dream.

In his twenties he became a professional reciter but was soon experiencing breathing and vocal problems which put his career in jeopardy. The treatments prescribed by doctors proved ineffective, as did their advice to rest his voice as much as possible between performances. Two medical advisors even recommended surgery on the vocal cords. He chose not follow this advice but instead started to question whether it was not something he was doing in using his voice that was causing the trouble. This proved to be a pivotal insight.

Alexander observed himself to see what he was doing while reciting. While using several mirrors to observe the alteration of his posture as he started to speak, he found he assumed a position associated with a fight or flight response; the result showed the head and neck poked forward of the shoulders, chin raised, head pulled back and down thus compressing the larynx. These days, this is many people's habitual posture and is accepted as normal.

After thorough experimentation, he developed a method of consciously sending messages to his body with his thoughts and intentions. For example, he sent a message to the neck to be free, to allow his head to extend forward and up and his back to lengthen and widen, in order to prevent the wrong habits kicking in. This, combined with refusing himself permission to speak until he could reliably maintain his enhanced posture in less demanding activities, gave him a way out of his troubles and led over many years to what we now recognise as the Alexander Technique.

Alexander soon started working with other actors, because they were impressed with the improvements he had made to the sonority and strength of his voice. He gradually found that his method for changing vocal habits had a more general application and helped a whole range of problems, from insomnia to arthritis, from asthma to problems with self-confidence and esteem, from back pain to post-operative recovery. He increasingly received referrals from doctors.

Tremendously excited by his discoveries and with the endorsement of an eminent doctor in Sydney he travelled to England in 1904 to spread his work further. In England he taught famous and distinguished people of the day, wrote four books to expound his ideas, and trained future teachers.[3]

While Alexander did 'cure' people of their physical and mental troubles, he saw himself as an educator giving people the tools of awareness and knowledge in order for them to help themselves. He felt very strongly that the work most needed was with children. If children can become aware of using their bodies skilfully and avoiding harmful tension, they can grow up well aligned and remain healthy and fit throughout life.

The main concept that underpins the Alexander Technique is that the way you think and move, in fact use your body in any fashion, affects your functioning and performance.

You can experience the Technique in group introductory courses and with one-to-one lessons. Your teacher will use gentle hands-on guidance and verbal explanations to help you find ease and balance within yourself in simple movements and everyday activities – such as sitting, standing, walking or bending. Through experience and observation you gain increased awareness enabling you to change longstanding habits and to function more efficiently.

In time you will be able to use your new understanding and skill in more complex and demanding activities. You can bring awareness and poise to anything you do, whether it be playing with your child, presenting at work or sitting well at the computer.

The Society of Teachers of the Alexander Technique (STAT) was founded in the UK in 1958 and now has affiliated societies worldwide. Teaching members are certified to teach the technique after successfully completing an approved full-time three year training course. Teachers adhere to the Society's Code of Professional Conduct, hold professional indemnity insurance and have enhanced Criminal Records Bureau (CRB) checks.

Building up integration

The Alexander Technique is learned through repetition of positive experiences of moving with increasing ease and lightness. One cannot take in all the information at once, particularly when your body is not giving you reliable information about your habitual patterns of tension. Who can ever say how they lost something? How would you lose anything deliberately? It's a contradiction, to know exactly how or where to place an object so that it is lost.

With Alexander work you will not know where your tension has disappeared to, and if it returns without you noticing, how to lose it again. But you will gradually know how to avoid acquiring it again. You will catch yourself in the act of pulling unnecessarily on your muscles and you will be able to refuse to do that. So if you find yourself with hunched shoulders, you will recognise that hunching is a deliberate act and you can refuse to continue hunching them. When you notice that every time you reach out to pick something up, you stick your chin out towards the object, you can refuse to cooperate with your habit of thrusting it forwards, and redirect your intention to release your neck and lengthen.

The fundamental part of this new learning is the part where you refuse to continue blindly on with old habits of restricted movement. Gradually you learn to integrate a better use of yourself with all the minutiae of daily living and the payoff is very rewarding.

Believe me, it is so comfortable to be free to breathe all of the time; it is so comfortable for the skeleton to support your weight. It's lovely to feel light. It helps you feel happy and trusting. Your confidence in yourself increases, your effectiveness is enhanced, your strength is increased.

Concepts in the Alexander Technique

Begin from neutral

'You know, sor, if I was going to Balbriggan I wouldn't be going from here at all' Old Irish saying

If that were said to you when you were in a desperate hurry to get to Balbriggan, late for a meeting, irritated with the endless traffic jams and with a tension headache from all the worry and stress, you might blow a fuse!

How many times do you find yourself in a situation where you are nowhere near where you should be and your day is appearing to conspire against you? Do you relax? Do you accept the inevitable, that you are going to be horrendously late? Do you turn around and go home? Not many of us have the presence of mind to accept the inevitable, so we continue racking up the tension, trying hard to be where we are not.

Alexander called this 'end-gaining'. By that he meant a futile and unreasoned attempt to force a result through unproductive over exertion and anticipatory tension, like revving the car without the gears being engaged, at the same time getting cross that you are going nowhere.

Well, when you are where you are, what's to be done about that? It would be great if we could suddenly become transformed into light, free, integrated and beautifully co-ordinated human beings. Then we would be in the right place to get where we want to go. Actually, we wouldn't be lost at all. Everything we undertook would be effortless and successful, not difficult or going in the wrong direction.

My advice is to get back into an emotionally neutral gear, stop revving the engine of your muscles and work out how to proceed from a more balanced state. It's never too late to change direction. All you need to do is to stop and consider your options. It's the stopping that is the powerful factor in your journey through life, whether for a momentary pause or a longer period of time.

All you need to do is Stop, Think, Act.

The head leads and the body follows

'The head and torso work together to condition the muscular elasticity of the whole body' Dr Theodore Dimon – Alexander Technique teacher and author

In my teaching room at school I have lots of pictures showing animals and birds in movement. The children and I talk about what we see in these pictures. For instance, the dog anticipaties a ball to be thrown and is backing away, ready to run after it. The dog's weight is asymmetrically placed, you can tell from its posture that it will run away from the camera. Its tail is wagging in joyous anticipation of the fun to be had.

There are several pictures of birds in flight. Their necks are extended, their beaks leading the way, wings flapping in strong strokes. Some are of birds coming to land, or to settle on water. One can see which birds are taking off and which birds are landing, from the angle of their bodies and placement of their feet.

There is a sequence of pictures of a cat falling from a height. The sequence shows how even though the cat starts off upside down, it will naturally rotate mid-air to land on its feet.

I ask the children what they see in common to all these pictures of birds and animals in movement, and they get it. All of them are leading with their eyes and heads.

We can learn much about movement if we watch animals. If they become badly co-ordinated through injury they are unlikely to survive in the wild. Their movement would be too clumsy and slow to protect them from predators.

We humans can get away with very poor co-ordination, cushioned as we are in our civilised culture. Basically the limits placed on freely co-ordinated movement are largely due to tension, specifically tension which stops the head leading and the body following.

The co-ordinating factor of the whole muscular system is setting up a harmonious relationship between the head, the neck and the back.

What do I mean by 'harmonious'? Well let's talk first about having a discordant relationship – one in which there is friction and stress. When an adult usually rises from a chair or bends to pick up something, the head is habitually retracted onto the top of the neck, pressing down on the spine and causing muscular strain and undue pressure. This is not natural. Animals only behave like this when they are cornered and in danger. They certainly do not habitually move with their heads pulled back and down into their bodies.

Giving attention to setting up a harmonious relationship – that of the head leading the body by extending upwards off the neck and back – is only necessary because you will need to overcome the habitual tendency to pull it back and down. Your conscious attention is required because habits are very strong and resistant to change.

Young children already have a harmonious relationship between their heads and backs. The danger is that they may lose the harmony and the relationship may become discordant. Through learning the Alexander Technique, this can be prevented.

Mechanical advantage

Remember what you learned about levers and pulleys at school? When you apply principles of leverage to yourself, particularly when you lift any weight, you know that you need to bend at the hips, knees and ankles using your legs rather than your back. If you are not paying attention to this, you are likely to bend your back when lifting, putting pressure on this vulnerable and overworked part of your anatomy.

You should take the same efficient body shape used when picking up a weight from a lower surface into doing any activity at a level lower than your normal reach. You see this in weight lifters and wrestlers who bend their legs to bend into a lower position. It is the same shape you would take to go into a squat or to sit down in a chair. Alexander called it the 'position of mechanical advantage', but as this is rather a mouthful, it is nowadays playfully referred to in the Alexander world as 'monkey'.

You can take a moment to consider how to put less pressure on your body and apply the leverage you need in all sorts of situations. Stop and think, for example, when you push a supermarket trolley. The inefficient way would be to crouch down over it and tense your legs to push down on the ground. Why is it inefficient? Because you contract your stomach muscles, pulling yourself towards the floor at the same time as tensing your legs to push you up off the floor. You still have to move the laden trolley round the supermarket, so you grip with your toes and force your tense body and heavy trolley forwards. Stop and think. The efficient way would be to stand tall and release your whole body weight forwards from your ankles. The weight of your body is likely to be greater than the weight of the trolley, such that the wheels start turning and off you go.

The importance of doing less

So if we all started life with a harmonious relationship between our heads and bodies, why have we lost it?

We shorten in stature over time. Stress, anxiety, fear and anger have a physiological effect on the body's musculature, which we find difficult to release. Animals are better at releasing their tension. Humans anticipate trouble and stiffen to be ready for it, yet are much less adept at forgetting the danger once it is past.

Shortening is a description for muscles that have been overworked for years and years and have become permanently stiff and unyielding. They have lost their elasticity and can become injured and sometimes cause pain. They have been doing too much and they can no longer let go.

The muscles of the neck should be there simply to balance and move the head, not to hold it down. In order for there to be minimum work in the neck, the skeleton must be allowed to do its job of supporting its own weight appropriately. If you ignore your bones, your muscles will step in with more tension to compensate.

The discordant relationship I have described is simply caused by doing too much or the doing the wrong thing with the wrong part. It interferes with optimum functioning of the body to support itself against the pull of gravity.

Emotions also play a large part in conditioning our reflexes. The body and the emotions are very involved with each other, you could say inseparable. Emotion is instantly registered as a change in body shape and tone.

Think of something burdensome. Have your shoulders sagged? Remember feeling anxious? What happened to your shoulders then? What happened to your heartbeat, breathing and to your facial expression? This is the stuff of being psycho-physical creatures. There is no separation between mental, emotional, and physical experiences – they all respond simultaneously.

A chronic fear response causes the person to stiffen and brace. What you see in some people's awkward postures is a muscular memory of fear, anger and anxiety carried into movement. We need to let go of emotions from the past and move on. We need to stay in the present.

The Alexander Technique provides the means to re-organise our responses. It is simply amazing how much recovery is possible if we let go of past fears and regrets and stop worrying and anticipating the future. It's really quite simple. The significant word is 'Stop'.

Stopping is a skill that takes practice. True stopping can happen in the midst of activity. It can happen anywhere and at any time. It is internal.

Awareness

A major part of the process of learning to 'Stop' is developing awareness. The ability to stop and do less starts with awareness. I start building awareness in teenagers by asking them to stop for a moment and listen to all the sounds around them without judging any of them. This is stilling to their busy, overloaded, chattering minds. They find it refreshing. They open their ears and listen in a way that perhaps they haven't listened since early childhood. To keep their attention from wandering into the thinking, planning and mind-wandering mode, I ask them to count the number of sounds they can hear one at a time and all together.

Awareness starts with pausing and giving yourself time. Time is such a valuable commodity and these days we all feel short of it. There is so much rushing about, so many deadlines to meet, timetables to be adhered to, journeys to be made in too little time to make them. Internal time can take very small portions of clock time and it can feel as if the world has opened up again. Even taking just a second to stop before acting can make a difference.

Give your children time too. Organise yourself and their day so that no-one has to rush. Have you noticed how fretful children can become when their routine is rushed and they don't have enough time?

Not rushing at home is an example of incorporating stopping time, thinking time so that action can take place more appropriately.

It matters how you do what you do

The way that you move and balance causes habitual postural tendencies. The Alexander Technique is based upon the idea that how you do what you do matters because 'use affects functioning'. By functioning, I mean all of your functioning as a human being, including your thinking, breathing, digestion, ease of movement, and ability to deal with stressful situations.

The Alexander Technique Directions

Emphasising unity of body and mind, Alexander formulated a set of instructions which can help to prevent unwanted habitual tensions and allow a more appropriate response. These have become commonly known as the Alexander Directions:

- Let the neck be free
- To let the head go forward-and-up,
- To let the back, lengthen and widen,
- And let the knees go forward-and-away

They are specific but don't include any instructions to lift, pull, hold, put or any other active verb. They are preventative, and create the conditions in which the right thing can do itself.

3. Not so common sense

The Alexander Technique points us in a direction that is not immediately obvious. However, when people come for lessons and experience the Technique, they exclaim, 'It's common sense when you think about it, but I just hadn't thought about it before'. It shows us that to allow free, balanced movement is our natural state of being and that to act in an unthinking and instinctive way can lead us into harmful patterns of behaviour.

Indirect means

I have talked about how unnecessarily complicated it would be to first weigh the body down with extra pressure on the spine and legs and then force movement against that downward pressure, but believe it or not, that's what modern humans do!

We have different types of muscle within the body. Some are outside of our direct control like the muscles of our heart, whilst others such as the biceps which we use to lift our arm are within our control. You simply think about an action that you want to do and the nervous system tells the muscles to act appropriately.

The muscles that move bones come in pairs, one to move the bone in one direction and the other to move it in the opposite direction. As one muscle (or set of muscles) contract, the other releases indirectly by reciprocal action. There is no direct way to lengthen a muscle, or to release muscle tension. When you are told to 'relax', there is no direct way that you can do this. You can only stop contracting and let the relaxation happen in its own time.

However, with the help of the Alexander Technique, we can voluntarily prevent unnecessary muscle contraction. If we begin this prevention by focusing on the head and neck area, the nervous system takes up the signals and communicates them to the rest of the body: Stop, Think, Act.

There are no direct means of improving your posture. Re-organising your posture deliberately and actively, from a template in your mind of which muscle should pull here and which muscle should pull there would be impossibly complex and is a little like putting the cart before the horse. Instructions like 'shoulders back, chest out, tummy in, stand up straight' simply don't work.

Alexander taught his pupils that their minds needed to be engaged in planning how they would carry out an action to avoid unnecessary tension. In particular, they must make sure the 'wrong' things (unnecessary habitual muscular holding and stiffening) were prevented. This was called 'the means whereby we gain our end'. The first command was to stop any immediate and unthinking action. They were taught to do nothing, to say 'No!' For children I have shortened this to, 'Stop, Think, and Act'.

Body Smile

One of the indirect ways of re-organising your posture originates with the basic idea that whatever you think has its physical counterpart. When you think anxious thoughts, your shoulders are very likely to reflect that by rising and hunching up around your neck. Try instead to think of smiling with your shoulders and upper chest. Try putting a smile around the back of your neck. Smile from ear to ear – at the back of your head! Imagine a smile between your hip bones or across your lower back. Become wreathed in smiles.

In this way, you will be able to bypass the intellect and get in 'under the radar'. Smiling is so natural a response that it is wired straight into the nervous system. You don't 'do' smiling, you feel pleasure and then you smile. You don't 'do' release of your postural muscles, you decide to stop tensing – you do nothing. Instead, invite your body to grow and the muscles will let go.

You could encourage children to open up and expand by saying:

Wait! Now let's grow tall. Smile with our bodies! Shazzan!

Don't just stand up straight: do nothing!

The next time you feel guilty about your posture and start to straighten your shoulders and lift up your chest, wait. Stop, Think, Act.

- First give yourself a pat on the back for becoming aware
- Next, breathe out and stop those anxious responses about being busy
- Smile across the front of your shoulders and around the back of your neck
- Imagine that your head can float up
- While you are imagining becoming lighter, think of dropping your nose a little
- Your head, balanced on top of the spine, will respond to gravity's pull, and will change its position ever so slightly, allowing your neck to lengthen

This is the Alexander way of improving your posture.

Alexander thinking

'Children must be taught how to think, not what to think' Margaret Mead – Anthropologist, writer and speaker

When Alexander teachers talk about thinking, they are not referring to intellectual activity, or to logical mental processes. Alexander thinking is a specific mental activity of pausing, of being aware and focusing intention before and during activity. You pause before lifting a heavy suitcase, remember your spinal alignment and bring your attention to the Alexander Directions. Instead of lunging forward to stoop and heave the suitcase up into the back of the car, you send your head forward and up, you bring your back up, away from your feet, releasing at the ankles, and releasing hip, knee and ankle joints, bend lightly and fluidly so that your hands reach the case handle, then bring your whole weight back to counterbalance the weight of the case and swing it off the floor and up into the boot of the car. Doesn't that sound complicated?

But actually, the description is a verbal slowing down of an action into its component parts. Had I described the activity of bending to pick up a heavy case your usual way, the description would have included the extra effort of shortening the body to do so. What is missing from this description of lifting the case with Alexander thinking, is the habitual shortening of your neck and torso, and the excessive force with which you would normally pull and push your legs. Including the Alexander Directions transforms the activity. Alexander Directions are streamlined and slim, like new technology. They are heaps more efficient than the old ways.

How you learn

'Learning, thought, creativity and intelligence are not processes of the brain alone, but of the whole body' Carla Hannaford – Author, biologist and educator

I believe that learning is largely associative and that the role of our senses and our movement in learning is of fundamental importance. What we first need to accept is that our senses are not necessarily like instruments that accurately measure and record objective data. Alexander called this problem 'faulty sensory appreciation'.

Do you ever catch sight of yourself in an overhead surveillance monitor and wonder 'Who's that? I don't see that person on this platform. Oh it's me! I didn't recognise myself'. Is the thought also accompanied by surprise that you are a different shape from what your feelings tell you? Are you more stooped than you expected? Or fatter? Do you then try and correct your imperfections by attempting to change to the opposite of what you see?

My son recently read a book on running and attempted to follow the instructions to the letter. He thought he had been very successful until he went on a course run by the author of the book. He was told that he had not succeeded in changing his running technique at all, that he was not moving his limbs in the way the book had instructed him. He had to acknowledge that he could not interpret what the words in the book would feel like. His subjective feelings of how successful he had been were unreliable. He was having to deal with faulty sensory appreciation.

What was needed for him was sensory feedback from an external source – an instructor. The new sensory experiences that he gained from the instructor's guidance helped him to make the changes required to improve his technique.

We all face the same issue of faulty sensory appreciation in trying to change any postural habit. Alexander himself took years to work it all out, but nowadays it's much easier with the help of a teacher.

It's also hard to learn when you are stressed. Stress is a reaction to a perceived threat. There is a chemical reaction to stress – an increase of cortisol (the 'stress hormone') in the blood stream. A noisy and stressful environment, or a constant state of worry adversely affect brain function, especially memory, increasing chronic levels of cortisol in the brain. These levels can prevent the brain from laying down a new memory, or from accessing already existing memories.

You owe it to yourself and to your children to moderate the amount of stress you are exposed to. However, you cannot totally eliminate stress and the crucial factor is looking at the way you respond to stress. Instead of responding by getting tense and worried, you can pause (Stop), free your neck (Think), let yourself breathe, accept the situation as it is and decide what the next step should be (Act). You might even laugh!

Take one step at a time

'How do you eat an elephant? One bite at a time'

We might just as well ask: 'How do you walk to the door?' And answer: 'Stop, Think, Act; free your neck and take one step at a time'.

When we learn something new, we can get information overload if it is all presented to us at once. Dr Shiniki Suzuki, the founder of the Suzuki Method for violinists, found that young children could learn to play the violin perfectly provided they were taken step by step from what they could already do. You are likely to have information overload right now about how to start putting the Alexander Technique into practice. Remember you can only go somewhere by starting from where you are. Your children can only go from where they are right now. What's the next step for you and your children?

First it will be helpful to understand the beginning and the process of positive child development.

4. Alexander and positive child development

'Our first consideration, therefore, in all forms of education must be in regard to securing for the child the highest possible standard of psycho-physical functioning during his attempts to master the different processes which make up the educational scheme. In this way the child will make a fair start, and, what is more to the point, he will continue to improve the conditions involved, hand in hand with his efforts as a pupil in all other spheres of activity' FM Alexander

Stages of development

Briefly, we are looking at overall stages of development throughout childhood. Of course, human development is more complex than I can describe here, but it is useful for you to know in general what to expect from your child. Development through the different stages will naturally overlap with the beginnings of the next stage, so here is an approximate map of the terrain.

The first stage

From birth until the age of seven, children are primarily interested in their motor skills – moving around, discovering and exploring objects. The natural pace of your child's motor development is not normally something that you will have to worry about. It typically takes place in its own time and way according to our human inheritance. Only if a child is brain damaged in some way will development be arrested or deviated, and that subject is beyond the scope of this book.

Watching new babies wriggle and stretch is fascinating. One is in awe of the potential of a newborn baby and every week one can witness developmental progress. During the first few months of life, babies learn how to co-ordinate movement so that their needs are met, they get to where they want to go and reach what they want. Before language develops, this is a matter of trial and error, the guide to their explorations being satisfaction and happiness. Children respond best to admiration, love and praise. When the baby first smiles, everyone is delighted and shows it by smiling back and loving the child more. The baby quickly learns what behaviour gets attention, a necessary skill for survival.

To begin with, the baby moves his arms and legs randomly, flexing and extending the trunk and limbs in identifiable reflex patterns. Then he discovers his hands and fingers, putting fingers into the mouth, waving them about to touch hanging objects. His skin is very sensitive to touch, particularly around the mouth and cheeks. As the developing brain makes more connections, the baby learns to roll and extend the trunk, forwards, backwards and sideways.

At the same time grasping objects becomes a fascination and is a motivator for movement along the ground, particularly if the object is a tiny bit out of reach. Stretching one arm forward at the same time as flexing the opposite leg, the baby begins to develop locomotion, which eventually becomes crawling, first on the belly, then supported by the knees and hands. The baby doesn't know how to do this – all he wants to do is to reach the object in which he is interested. His idea includes an 'action intention and an outcome' and his brain responds to these signals by activating the body's musculature towards what he wants.[4] So he wriggles about, flexing and extending until his body has wriggled its way towards the fascinating object. This builds strength and co-ordination throughout the body.

Soon babies can raise themselves up and twist into a sitting position. From a sitting position babies can transfer quickly and easily back into crawling forward. Bottoms are raised in the air, feet to the floor, and the baby very gradually acquires the strength to support himself on his feet with his hands resting on a firm surface. Finally, the baby learns to rely on the feet alone, taking sideways steps with the occasional support from his hands until unsupported walking becomes possible. This is when the baby will often lose balance, sitting suddenly with surprise, instinctively throwing his head forward in the moment of falling. A baby rarely falls backward hitting his head.

It is important not to cut out the process of learning balance and alignment by constantly standing your baby on his feet, before his balance is acquired through the natural process of postural development.

Once the infant can stand and walk, hands become free for doing things and co-ordination between hands and eyes rapidly develops. Making sounds is something the baby will do from the very earliest age and these sounds eventually become recognisable as rudimentary communication. Talking naturally follows, particularly if the child lives with friendly communicative people and is read to frequently.

Children start talking by naming things: flower, dog, cat, bus, and by naming images of familiar things in books. They are working with pattern recognition. The most basic of recognisable patterns are two eyes and a mouth.

At two and a half, Sammy is very happy putting sticks into the ground and taking them out again, putting stones into a container and then putting them into another container, building towers of blocks, pushing the train around the track and the buses along the edge of the tabletop. He doesn't need a reason. It's just fun and absorbing doing these things.

As his imagination develops, he plays with the names of things. 'What's this Mummy?' says Sammy, following the example constantly set him by his mother throughout his little life. 'It's an apple' says his mother. 'NO' replies Sammy. 'It's a … an orange' Mummy counters 'It's a spoon' … ' NO MUMMY, NO,' says Sammy getting upset. 'Well what is it Sammy?' 'It's only … only … only … an apple". Rather bemused, his mother wonders what this new game is about.

Another time she decides to play along. 'What's this Mummy?' asks Sammy. 'It a wiggle woggle' she says. 'No' Sammy replies, 'it's a piggle poggle'. 'It's a wonky waggle' says his mother and so the game goes on until Sammy finally has had enough. 'NO MUMMY. It's a banana'.

proved himself right again! More importantly, he is beginning . that he and his mother are separate beings with separate opinions.

Children create stories around their activities. Vehicles go so fast crashes occur, trains go through tunnels, towers fall down, the ambulance has to be called, the fire engine puts out the fire. A bucket filled with water, mud and stones becomes a milk shake that mummy has to drink. A young child is deep in his fantasy world where the impossible can easily and frequently happen. All this play mimics real life and prepares them for it.

Nursery years are focused on activities that develop more refined motor skills and physical balance as well as feeding children's imagination. Eventually hand/eye co-ordination is so well developed that writing is taught, along with recognising words and the rules of spelling.

The second stage

During the second stage of development, children begin to acquire social and emotional understanding and range.

My daughter had an imaginary friend who was never to be left behind when we went on holiday. Gradually she became better able to distinguish between fantasy and reality and better able to draw on her own experience, taking material from her everyday life into her play.

At four, my grand-daughter Sophie was practicing role play at being the caring adult. 'Go to sleep grandma, go to sleep now'. 'WAKE UP!' she would shout. 'You need your medicine. You're poorly and need to go to the hospital'. This was following an incident where she was admitted to hospital for a deep cut to her knee. She continued for some years to develop and refine her caring skills, caring for her little brother and becoming very responsible.

Children ask numerous questions at this age, starting at first to ask 'why' to everything. Gradually the questions become more discerning and the child asks more particular questions in her quest to understand better how the world around her functions. These questions will often explore sex and the differences between boys and girls and how babies are made.

Sometimes there is a need to play out what has been troubling them, to expunge it from their unconscious fears. Life is still scary for them, and although they are developing self-reliance and confidence, they need the protection of an adult who can judge better than they are able to, what the dangers really are. Well established routines help them feel secure.

At five, Sophie became afraid of dogs and their natural exuberance, wanting to jump into my arms in the park, cowering behind me even if the dog in question was a hundred yards away. She wasn't able to judge the distance or timing of the perceived threat. Children are not safe to cross roads until after they are seven, due to this inability to judge distance and time.

At six, the child is experimenting with her emotional range finding and with her choices. Mummy is buying yoghourt in the supermarket. 'I really, really don't like it and even if you buy it I WON'T EAT IT', she shouts, pouting and sulking, her face a picture of petulance and misery, her body sagging, her feet dragging. This over-reaction happens because she lacks the judgement to know what degree of force she needs in order to get her Mummy to hear her. This would be an opportunity to help her see another person's point of view as well as her own.

Gradually children develop more understanding of what others may be feeling. First it's expressed as kindness to their toys or the new baby, though the newborn may be in danger of being smothered by an inappropriate display of affection!

Older children like to acquire facts. They form collections: of pictures, tickets, and information. They are interested in potential: the potential of what they can do with words, the potential of how strong they are. They are testing themselves and learning to discriminate. Through these processes, they learn about boundaries: of their strength and of their behaviour. Often they will overstep the mark. This is all part of the learning process.

The third stage

Later development is more brain oriented. Complex mental skills and conceptual thinking develop in the teenager. They become more reasoned, more understanding. They start to have a grasp of how the wider world works and they can readily see the point of easing their lives by losing some of their tension.

The teenagers at school love to lie down on my Alexander Technique teaching table during their lesson. They say that it's the best fifteen minutes in the week. It allows them time just to be. Nobody is demanding anything from them and they can rediscover the non-verbal parts of themselves and open their awareness to sounds and sights. It's truly refreshing for them. Every time they deliberately don't help me, they get congratulated. They are learning to say 'no' and that empowers them. They can then think how to proceed without tension and with clear direction.

They think it's 'cool' to show their friends the game of how to walk their fingers up a wall and grow taller and taller, then to bring them down again remaining at their full height. They like to experiment with the game of copying the walks of people in front of them and feeling how unusual these other ways of walking are compared to their own. Each person thinks of themselves as being normal. I point out to them that nobody is normal in that sense. We are just used to our own ways.

For example, a boy who is growing into an adult faster than his body sense can keep pace with, having realised that trying to straighten his shoulders is ineffective, chooses to square off his shoulders by raising his arms and then letting them drop without his body sagging back into its usual place. It proves to him how wide and strong he really is, not a little boy any more.

Early years

A child is born with some survival reflexes and more develop in the early years of life. Each reflex is built on the foundation of the earlier matured reflexes. However trauma, illness and unhappiness can stop the earlier reflex maturing to its full extent. The later reflex is then founded on an immature reflex and the foundation is unsound.

Mike Cross, Alexander Teacher and Neuro-Developmental Therapist, has made a direct connection between Alexander's directions and the basic life saving reflexes which, in healthy development, are inhibited by the development of the higher brain centres. What remains generally unrecognised is how many of us still suffer from aberrant, immature reflexes. These cause undue reactions to any stimulus that we unconsciously perceive to be unexpected or threatening.

Unhelpful reactions are those that limit and prevent development happening in an appropriate and timely manner. What seems to happen to human beings is a psychological and physical restriction aroused by fear. This takes place at a subconscious level but has resonance throughout the human organism. Thus, an infant who experiences major shocks or repeated threats to its safety such as a withdrawal of its mother's reassurance, will store the memory and employ defences which are appropriate to its stage of development and central nervous system functioning. This reaction can persist throughout life and interferes with the proper functioning of the nervous system and has been well identified in the study of aberrant reflexes.[5]

Alexander teacher Ray Evans described the Technique as 'Vestibular Re-education'. He proposed that the Alexander Technique can help correct the reflexes that have been interrupted in their development and correct vestibular balance functioning. It is not unknown for people having Alexander lessons to notice profound changes in their functioning and sense of self, as though something very basic has clicked into place.

The development of movement

Infants and small children demonstrate co-ordinated movement patterns learned incrementally from birth, through positions of spinal support to an independent stance and unsupported movement on two feet. Throughout this developmental process they explore balance, progressing gradually from their learned patterns towards the more advanced states of co-ordination. Except, as we have seen, infinitesimal interferences to normal development are continually taking place through childhood, reflecting the build up of 'character structure' and defence patterns.[6]

Human life may be full of trauma, illness and unhappiness and compensatory mechanisms come into play to cope with the resulting inadequacies. That's just the stuff of life. But you, as a parent, can be attentive to lessening the background stress and urgency of your family life. You can provide a learning environment which is safe yet not overprotective. You are there to avert an accident, not to caution your child constantly or play into their fears, which might cause them to stiffen in defence.

This is the first way you can help improve your child's posture. It really depends on your own ability to stop and think before acting.

Movement creates intelligence

Every stage of your child's motor development fosters creativity and nurtures brain development. Research in the USA has shown that children who crawl have better memories, are quicker at languages and more adaptive to learning specific skills.[7] Everything we do depends on the fluidity of our co-ordination.

You can allow your child's development to proceed in its own time and its own way. The flow of development follows its own internal path and works itself out. It's natural and effortless. All you have to do is to stand back and watch the process unfold. Don't be tempted to rush the process of your child's natural development by helping your child to skip any inconvenient steps such as crawling. Crawling is vital for healthy development, both of the brain and for the support muscles of the back.

If you want your child to have the best chance to grow up with good postural habits into a well behaved, skilful and clever individual, all the developmental steps should take place in the right sequence and at the appropriate time for that child. You let it happen in its own time and way. There is an old-fashioned phrase: 'nature knows best', and in this case, it's true. Don't interfere with nature. This is the second way you can help improve your child's posture.

Wait! Now let's grow tall. Smile with our bodies. Shazzan!

Don't rush the process

Trust that the development of each of your children will have its own pace and momentum. Each child has an individual pattern. Some will talk sooner, some will acquire impressive motor skills, one baby will still be crawling while another of the same age will have already been walking for a while. It's very difficult for mothers and fathers when meeting other families, to avoid comparisons between one child and another. Competition rears its ugly head! This competition is nowhere more apparent than in encouraging a baby to stand upright well before her muscles and co-ordination are ready. The immediate reward for you is that beam of delight as she is praised and admired by all, but as I stated previously, it may not be so helpful for longer term development.

The danger here is that your baby will associate the psycho-physical feeling of standing with an unready back (that slight feeling of sag and strain) and will accept that feeling as the norm. She is not in a position to question her experience.

Rather than being over eager for your baby to stand and walk early, allow her to roll and crawl and pull herself up to standing when she is ready. This will all happen naturally and at the right time for the development of her co-ordination and will nurture the development of her brain. The message from the Alexander Technique is 'let the right thing do itself'.

This is the third way you can help improve your child's posture.

The 'how' of doing things

Once your child can walk and talk, and particularly if you have allowed the process of physical development to unfold in its own time and way, the next few years are the most fertile time for laying down the ground rules of the Alexander Technique. You will already be establishing rules of manners and greetings, you will be nearing the end of the terrible twos and your toddler is recognising that he or she has a personality that is separate from yours. If you are wise, your lifestyle is predictable and rhythmic, meals are taken regularly, pre-school is attended a few days a week and life has a pattern to which your child is accustomed.

I suggest that you make up a little ritual that you use often in the year before your child attends primary school. The pattern is this: you include your boy or girl in saying out loud, 'I have a secret that I will teach you. It's this: When you can't immediately make something work, or you can't immediately have something you want, we say: *Wait! Now let's grow tall. We smile with our bodies. Shazzan!* Now it will be easier'. My daughter used to smile at red traffic lights to turn them green. Of course it always worked, even though sometimes that took time!

All the minor frustrations in daily life are good opportunities for the practice of this ritual. When the key won't easily open the door: Wait! Now let's grow tall! Smile with our bodies. Shazzan! When all the groceries fall back out of the cupboard when you have just put them in: Wait! Now let's grow tall! Smile with our bodies! Shazzan! When you can't open the jam jar: Wait! Now let's grow tall! Smile with our bodies! Shazzan!

All through this section, I have drawn your attention to focus on not losing the natural grace and co-ordination that is constantly present in the baby and young child. By not interfering with what is already proceeding according to developmental lines you will maintain the natural poise your child displays. 'Wait, grow, smile' teaches your child not to interfere with poise when things are not proceeding as smoothly as hoped. Frustration, anger, and impatience all create tension. Much of that tension is mis-applied, the force is directed inward rather than outward, into the self instead of out to the object.

It is best to establish this attitude to solving minor problems before your child reaches school age. You cannot expect to be able to protect your child all of the time, so methods of dealing with life need to be taught at home. This is the most vital teaching of all – how to deal with oneself.

Children are very robust internally. The ideal would be never to lose their lightness and poise but that's not a realistic expectation. In the early years of a child's life, poise is never far off and is easily recoverable. Poise stems from happiness and joy, rest and refreshment. Natural healthy qualities, only lost in extreme deprivation, sorrow and continuous strain. You can teach your child how to recover poise quickly. The secret is to: 'Wait! Grow tall, smile with the body'.

By teaching them this, you are teaching them the how of physical and mental activity.

Primary years

The next big influence comes when your child attends nursery or primary school. For some babies this is the norm from six months old. Staff at the nursery look after the children's needs and allow them to play with specially designed toys and interact with each other. Their hand/eye co-ordination develops as they build towers, push toy cars and draw or paint. At the primary level, reading, writing and learning facts are added into the mix.

What I want to emphasise here is how the learning process is a total psycho-physical experience. It is really important for children that they learn body management along with the development of their mental skills. I fear that this is too often neglected and not enough attention is paid by staff to the way children sit to listen and learn, the way they run and walk, lift objects, climb ladders and generally balance themselves. Too much attention is paid to the results of what they are attempting, not enough attention is paid to how they manage their bodies while busy with these activities.

Best time to start

The best time to start focusing on your child's posture is in early childhood. Natural poise and good co-ordination often become impaired as soon as children attend primary school, and sometimes earlier. Very quickly, sitting still in a group affects children's posture. They return to the primary curves of infancy, relaxing and becoming inward in their attention while listening to the teacher, and while reading and writing. This return to infancy is likely to lessen their alertness. Instead, I would suggest that they remain outwardly interested, as the infant is when reaching out to grasp objects. If the teacher accompanies circle time with songs and activities and reminds the children to stay tall and smiley, it will naturally follow that their attention will be better balanced.

Unfortunately, in primary education, with its emphasis on separating out the brain from the body, and over emphasising the importance of brain learning, by the time children are aged five to six, they are already incorporating slump and unnecessary tension into their concentration habits.

Remember that studies have proved that brain and body support each other in the learning process.[8] The brain becomes more able, more intelligent, and more retentive when mental processes are supported by a well-balanced body.

Provide suitable furniture

Chairs play an important part in a child's school life. Some provision is made to supply the smallest chair for the youngest pupils and the sizes tend to be graded every two years of school age. But children grow at different rates and children particularly tall or small for their age use the same size as all the others.

At home, children are very often required to sit on adult sized chairs, their legs dangling uncomfortably and with the table height also at an unsuitable level for the child's height. While this cannot always be helped, if children write or draw for any length of time, they can develop bad habits of putting their heads sideways or on the tabletop and twisting their bodies uncomfortably. If not corrected they will hold their crayons and pens with too much force and tension. Teach them how hold a pen or crayon without gripping tightly, and to apply only just enough pressure to other objects by reminding them to: 'Wait! Grow tall! Smile with the body!' Remember to do this yourself too.

The rhythm of your life

I watched a woman with a baby on her hip. Lively music was playing over the loudspeaker and she was bouncing the baby up and down to it in time to the music and swaying around. I thought to myself: that child will grow up to have a good sense of rhythm and movement; his mother is teaching him at every moment to respond to music just by doing that with him.

Now let's look at the ordinary things that you and your children do every day. You get up, wash and dress. Do you ever ask yourself 'How am I doing this?' I suspect that these actions are automatic, pre-programmed years ago and taken totally for granted. In normal family life this time of getting ready for the day is often the most rushed and stressful. It doesn't seem logical that we try to take such care of our babies, being calm and gentle with them, yet are so tight and stressed in ourselves. The unfortunate thing is that, like the baby held by his mother moving to the rhythm of music, our children move to our rhythm throughout their childhood, whatever that rhythm is like. If the rhythm of childhood is one of rush, hurry and tension, they will internalise that and it will become their habit as well.

Here again, in the early years, as you help your child to wash and dress, you can both: *'Wait; grow tall; smile with your body; celebrate each minor stage. Shazzan!'* If you have already adopted these methods as a way in which you tackle doing things, you will only have to remind your children as they become more and more independent in following these methods.

Secondary years

The transition to secondary school, with its bigger and wider environment and its promise of more scope for science, sport and music, is an exciting prospect, one that is often made without undue trouble. Your child settles in quickly, makes new friends and adapts to the challenge of changing classrooms for each lesson and meeting new staff. There is likely to be more homework too, and he or she must be more independent and remember sports kit, books and instruments on the right days of the week, or there may be detentions and other punishments as a result of forgetting or not having work ready on time.

Teenage struggles

At this time, your child's body and brain are beginning to change dramatically. Neuroscientists have only recently been able to study the re-organisation of the brain in adolescence, and what they are finding is that the frontal lobes, which are the part of the brain involved in reasoning, planning, and impulse control, not only grow, but rearrange themselves, with some consequent breakdown of the cognitive function that was present before puberty. While this is happening, the teenager may appear disorganised and inconsistent: organisational skills, decision making and the ability to set priorities, can be severely affected. Teenagers may become vulnerable to risky behaviour; they experience the brain, body and social self as being out of phase with each other, their co-ordination can suffer greatly, they can find it really difficult to set priorities.

This intense pressure and speed of change comes at the most demanding time of their school life. Not only do they need more sleep, but hormonal changes set their body clocks to later timing; they are awake until late and then have difficulty waking up to be ready for school. As a result they can become sleep deprived and the pressure of deadlines, exams, sporting events and social life can over-extend their capacities severely. Some studies indicate that the functioning of the brain in adulthood is conditioned by what teenagers apply their minds to throughout this period; it makes a difference to overall later brain function if they spend hours playing computer games, or learning history, or hours playing sport or studying a musical instrument.

It's no wonder teenagers have a reputation for being moody, inward looking or lacking in confidence. The most intense pressure of their lives comes at the most psycho-physically difficult stage.

Feeling loved and wanted at home, close to people at school and fairly treated by teachers, helps teenagers feel connected. Connectedness lowers the likelihood of emotional distress that may lead to substance abuse, violence, suicide or early sexual activity. In addition, being able to discuss issues that arise with a close friend of the family or other respected adult, helps the teenager to apply more fore-thought to their decision-making and helps them understand better the likely consequences of certain actions. They become more able to stop, think, and then act. The earlier this is introduced to them in their life, the easier it is to apply it in the teenage years.

Natural poise

Teenagers who have developed and maintained their natural poise are the most likely to weather the storms of adolescence and feel connected with themselves and others. Poise involves letting go of the past and not rushing into the future. Poise requires immediacy of attention. It arises when everything happens at the right time and in the right place. All of the above will be improved over time through the use of the Technique. It is something you learn for yourself and it is an entirely natural process of self-improvement.

With your love and support, your children can fulfil and keep expanding their potential. This requires poise in daily living. Don't rush, don't hurry onto the next thing, the next stage, before the present stage is developed. So often problems occur in our impatience to move on, to acquire more, to get more done.

As parents, we are always trying to help our children be the best they can be. It comes naturally to be both protective and to show the way. This can best be done by keeping yourself in balance, and encouraging your teenager to maintain balance as best as possible throughout the turbulent years of change and development. You maintain your balance by stopping, thinking to grow, then you are ready to act in a different way.

The poised and well-co-ordinated child will be able to:

- Stay crossed legged on the floor without slumping
- Squat easily
- Raise both arms to the side at an equal height
- Balance on one leg with minimal tipping to the side
- Touch the opposite knee: right hand to left knee, left hand to right knee, without confusion
- Sit at a computer without slumping
- Move with fluidity and speed
- Breathe with mouth closed
- Work hard without getting headaches or back pain
- Write in an open upright position
- Pick something up by bending the knees and hips
- Stand with ears, shoulders, hips and ankles vertically in line with each other

It's never too late!

Young bodies and minds are extremely plastic and adapt quickly. You can begin to help your children improve their posture when they are in middle school, or even when entering teenage, by setting the examples you wish them to follow.

You can help your children's posture in the following ways:

- Develop their sense of themselves in a positive and affirming way
- Heighten your children's awareness of where they are in the room
- Heighten their awareness of other people in close proximity
- Ask them to listen to the sounds they can hear, and look for colours and shapes they can see
- Ask them to tell you what sensations they can feel
- Feed in basic ideas about staying tall and smiley to eat
- Draw their attention to staying tall and smiley to write
- Heighten their awareness of how they are doing what they are doing

5. Mapping the body

'The child is always attracted by machinery; indeed, to find out 'how it works' is the natural desire of every healthy child ...' FM Alexander

It's surprising how little we really know about how our brains and bodies function. As long as they work together fairly smoothly and produce adequate results, there's a general idea that 'if it ain't broke, don't fix it'. We often don't even have a very clear idea of where the different body parts are or what they can and cannot do. It may help to have some basic information about how things might 'get broke' and why they may need fixing.

Eliminate strain

Did you know that bad posture is an active muscular state? Far from being a state of being too relaxed and therefore having to pull the body up straight, it is an imbalance of muscular tension, pulling the body out of alignment. This strain to pull yourself up straight adds to the effect that gravity has on the body, further compounding the problem.

What's remarkable is that the body's postural reflexes, if left to do their work without interference, respond to the gravitational pull by lengthening upwards! So the reflex response to gravity is to extend upwards. Moreover this reflex feels effortless. This can be seen in the small child, who bobs along, appearing to bounce off his feet.

Since good posture is less a matter of doing the right thing than avoiding doing the wrong thing, you don't have to work hard to have good posture. You can relax, but upwards! Let the healthy reflexes in your body do their work of taking you up.

Long muscles contract efficiently

When you become tense, your muscles become unduly shortened. Short muscles have less length and so are less efficient in their contractive ability. When your muscles are already contracted throughout your body, much of your strength is tied up in maintaining this state. This is why sports people stretch before activity, and again afterwards. Long muscles contract efficiently. Remember to lengthen your muscles by the indirect means of letting go of your muscles and relaxing your head upwards.

Improve balance

Relaxing upwards will improve your balance. An adult head weighs an astonishing four to five kilos. The head, being so heavy, has a very important role to play in the balance of the body. If it tips too far in any direction on the neck, you will need to hold on to it quite hard to stop its weight tipping you over. In all cases it has a drastic effect on the curves in the spine. Imagine falling asleep in the train or on a car journey. If your head is unsupported, it will flop uncomfortably, waking you up.

Increase freedom

What the head needs in order to stay poised on the top of the spine, is freedom from over-constraint of the neck musculature. Rather like the story of Goldilocks and the three bears, there is a point where your neck is just right, not too soft, not too hard. It is this dynamic of head balance on the neck that organises your postural support.

To regain this natural poise, you will have to unlearn your old habits of tensing and tightening, those habits that were built up to defend you from real or imaginary attack. This is most easily done with an Alexander teacher in a one-to-one situation. However, using the ideas in this book you can help yourself improve your posture.

You can experiment with increasing your awareness in a playful way, not with trying hard to be right. It continues with adopting lighter attitudes, a lighter way of holding objects, a lighter way of bending to pick things up, a lighter way of walking about. It involves consciously refusing to respond immediately to the triggers that tighten you up and pull you down. It's all about stopping and thinking before you act.

Incredible lightness of being

Your children display this lightness when they are very young. Some even continue to stay light into their teens, moving as if they are suspended above the ground. Don't you envy them? Instead of the adult cumbersome and heavy modes of moving, falling into chairs with a thump, groaning when bending down to pick up a pen, or holding their painful backs to ease the spasms, many children move lightly and freely. When still, they are able to move again at the slightest stimulus, bending easily with both feet on the floor to examine a toy or crumb, or sitting on the floor in one fluid movement.

There can come a time when children start to think of the structure of their bodies, particularly if they complain of aching or hurting in different parts. Injuries caused by falling or bumping into things heal quickly, but children often fear that they will continue to hurt for a long time. Even three days of stiffness after strenuous exercising can seem an age to a child! Longer-term injuries caused by misuse, will best be solved by giving children information and positive encouragement to help themselves. They need to understand the source of the misuse and how their habits can cause them strain. They need the self-knowledge to recognise how to maintain their lightness and the rule of stopping, thinking, and only then acting.

You can start to teach your children how to maintain their lightness, by first teaching them how their bodies are constructed, where the different parts are and what influences what within them. This can be done through a process of 'body mapping'.

Body Mapping

Most people don't have an accurate mental map of their own bodies. Think about your own body for a moment and see if you can answer these questions:

- Where does your head sit on your neck?
- Where does your neck begin and end?
- Which way does your diaphragm move?
- Which part of your spine would you include as your backbone?
- What parts of your anatomy would you include in your back?
- Where are your hip joints?
- How many movements do your upper arms allow?

Experiment with your children. See what moves forward and back or from side to side, and from which joint, or have a look at pictures of a skeleton to find out the answers. Children usually find the skeleton fascinating. Play with your children's and your own posture. Get it all wrong! Hunch up and curl over, stiffen your legs, hold your breath, screw up your faces, make yourself really uncomfortable! Try expanding out of those restricted states, like an inflatable cushion. Get too puffed up, do it too much. Come back into a more neutral state of rest and release. These games will help restore your equilibrium.

It is really useful to have a picture in your head of the parts of your body, corresponding with the feeling of where it is.[9] In my teaching, I sometimes find that it is as if some parts of a person's body are invisible to them, because they have blocked the feeling of that part for so many years with heavy ways of moving it. They have lost the location, rather like forgetting where your friend lives after too many years of not visiting their home.

Importance of head balance

Your head pivots on the top of your spine. What you see as your head in the mirror is your skull plus your jaw. Your head is heavier in front of the pivot point. Strong muscles up the back of your neck hold the head in place but sometimes they work too hard and hold the head back too far. As Alexander teachers, we call this pulling the head back and down. Not only does this have an effect on the head, but it compresses the whole body as well. This contrasts with what we see in infants. Their disproportionately large heads are freely poised and are falling forwards, tipping their bodies over their feet yet extending and stretching the spine upwards and stimulating their postural reflexes, maintaining balance.

You can't see all of the muscles behind the facial bones. Tiny muscles between the head and the top of the spine are intricately connected to the way in which you balance. Alexander discovered the importance of head-neck balance in wanting to resolve his vocal and breathing problems. Head balance is also affected by the musculature of your tongue, jaw, eyes, and hearing. If you tense any of this musculature in a habitual way, such as grinding your teeth, or fixing your gaze on a computer screen for hours, you may adversely affect your head-neck balance and therefore your co-ordination.

It's surprising how quickly children get into the habit of tensing their faces, tongues, jaws, eyes and holding their breath. This can be seen in primary school when, if their posture is uncorrected, they try and get their mouths close to their hands to facilitate the translation of speech into writing. Quickly this habit becomes associated with writing and is carried into adulthood unquestioned. Their bodies are still pliable so they can easily relax again in play and movement, but the memory of 'this is how I write' remains and gradually, that natural pliability becomes less elastic and responsive. Neck musculature, in particular, acquires a habitual tendency to shorten and to remain shortened, whatever activity is undertaken.

Spinal curves

Because the curves of the spine are balanced between back and front and from side to side, shortening in one part of the spine causes a ripple effect of shortening right through and results in lordosis, kyphosis or scoliosis. Attempts to correct this tendency generally focus on static posture, standing up straight, or on corrective exercises rather than thinking dynamically. We should look at posture in a different way.

In the spine there are two basic curves. The first can be described as primary. It is a total flexion of the spine, the position a very new baby will be in when held by her mother against her chest. Professor Raymond Dart (1893–1998), anatomist and anthropologist, named it the foetal curve and emphasised that this curve is absolutely basic. A secondary curve (cervical) comes about as the infant is placed on her stomach and lifts her head. It is the interplay between these two curves that gives rise to movement patterns in the infant, and therefore in the adult.

The primary curve comes about when focusing on the inner world of self, whereas the secondary curve is more about your intent to reach out into the world to follow a point of interest. We can look at posture as a tension pattern arising from an emphasis on moving from over-extension of the spine (an emphasis on the secondary curve and one encouraged by army training) and the foetal curve of flexion (the recognisable teenage slump).

This way of looking at posture removes the stigma of labelling any position as bad but recognises the dynamic use of the whole body in action. Posture does not mean a fixed position, but is a much more dynamic and poised way of being.

I question whether direct approaches such as 'stand up straight' can address habitual psycho-physical responses. What actually happens when a person wants to reach for something, get up from a chair or run for the bus? They will rely on the inbuilt, learned responses of shortening the neck and pulling the head back and down as they attend to the action, reinforcing their habitual use.

Say 'No!' to pulling the head back and down. Say 'Yes!' to sending it 'forward-and-up'. It's rather like balancing a ball on your finger – the finger has to keep moving to be constantly underneath the ball. This is what's happening to your postural reflexes as you stand still. They are constantly monitoring and adjusting to your balance. They will do this more easily if they are free, not rigid.

Bony landmarks

'Bony landmarks' is a useful concept in teaching children how to let their bones support them and give muscles a rest. Our bony landmarks are the places where bones lie near the surface of the body and support weight. Thus, the main area of bony support when standing are the bones of the feet (base of the big toe, side of the foot and heel, like the wet footprint you make on coming out of the shower). When we are sitting, the bony supports are the sit-bones, (two of them at the base of the pelvis), on which we can rock and sway. You can easily feel your sit-bones if you sit down on top of your fingers on a hard chair!

When we lie on our backs, the bony supports are the back of the head, the shoulder blades, and the pelvis and the feet when the knees are bent up and feet flat on the floor.

One way of getting children to stop before action is to tell them to think of their bony landmarks first. With very young children, you could say 'Where are your feet? Can you point them toward the window? Can you point them to the door? Can you point them towards Mummy now and keep them still while I put on your coat?'

You can make up little games like this, working up the body until they can find their ears and point them to the ceiling while they sit at table or on the floor.

Let your bones support you

A vital part of the process of re-organising your body involves your awareness of weight and bony alignment.

Your musculature can rest if you let your bones support you, one vertebra on top of another, weight evenly distributed on the bony landmarks. Muscles have to work harder when the spine is unduly curved over, or curled up unevenly.

It is useful to imagine that it is not your muscles that do the work of supporting you and keeping you upright, but your bones. Your bones provide the skeletal framework around which your muscles are wrapped. Muscles are there to move the bony framework around.

Joints

Bony landmarks enable us to locate our main joints for bending the body. People are particularly vague about where their hip joints are located. When I ask my pupils to point to their hip joints, many of them will touch the bones at the top of the pelvis, the iliac crests. The hip joints lie a lot lower than you might think, at the bottom of the pelvis, around pocket level of your trousers or where you crease your leg when you lift up your knee. It's really helpful to know this, otherwise you misguidedly try and bend at your lower back level and hold the whole of the pelvis with your legs. Inevitably you will miss your sit bones and sit with the pelvis slid forwards! I saw a lad sitting like this only yesterday. He was practically lying in the bus stop shelter he was so horizontal. People think that this is relaxed but if you only consider what the flexor muscles of the abdomen, legs and the back of the neck have to do to maintain that position for any time you'd be astonished that you could assume it is relaxing.

Although your spine is jointed, it is not designed to bear weight in an exaggerated, bent over position, and so your muscles must pull and heave, putting strain on the spine and pinching nerves. Not only that, slumping interferes with our breathing and digestion. It is really helpful to think instead that our bones support us; our muscles are there to move those bones around. Your bones are your support structure and your muscles are like a suit. Most of us, unfortunately, wear the suit badly.

Helping your children stay free

Here is a summary of what you have learned so far about helping your children stay free:

- Let the strength of your baby's back develop through crawling
- Ensure your touch remains light and free by growing light yourself
- Teach them to Stop, Think, Act
- Bring their attention into the present
- Remind them to wait and grow
- Provide suitable furniture
- Remind them to grow tall and smiley to write or eat or to run and climb
- Keep them active. Take them out to bounce in bouncy castles, on trampolines, to swing and slide, do handstands and forward rolls, to balance on bars and climb up ropes
- Play with posture

Alexander was passionate about the importance of his work with regard to children, to help them achieve their potential and avoid unnecessary health problems. He set up a school in the 1930s, the 'Little School', where the children all learned to make time for a moment so that they could give their directions to free their necks and send their heads forward and up, in whatever activity they were engaging in.[10]

Here is what Peter, who attended Alexander's Little School, said: *'If anybody asks me a question I must stop and not answer at once so as to give me time to order my head to go forward and up to speak.'*[11] Another pupil wrote this poem: [12]

Untitled by J. Bradbridge

There once was a girl who said 'Yes'
Why I've got to say 'No' I can't guess
I just won't say 'No'!
I'll sit down anyhow

Though I'll get in a terrible mess!
There once was a girl who said 'No'
I'm not going to sit down and so
I'll tell my head 'forward-and-up'
Before I sit down to sup
But I'm not going to sit down. Oh No!

Today more is known about psychology and how children learn best. Children will copy the behaviour of adults they love and respect. You are the dearest and most loved of all the adult role models who influence your children. They look up to you to set them the example of how to behave and how to develop their psycho-physical skills for self-control. They will copy your ability to take time to assess the situation and work out the best means for achieving the necessary result. Taking time is as important as saying please and thank you – constant parental reminders are needed for the 'magic words' to become a habit. The magic words here are an adaptation of 'Stop, Think, Act' – they are 'Stop and grow'. An example might be: 'Would you like a biscuit?', 'Yes please, Mummy', 'Stop and grow then'.

When your child is showing you how good he is at running or at ball games, you could say to him, 'Try aiming for the sky as you run. You'll run even faster!' 'Try thinking tall as you kick the ball rather than just trying to get it into the goal'. You see, it makes everything easier. There will be lots of practical opportunities such as this – mixing things in a bowl, pushing a trolley, building bricks, running and jumping, opening a door, kicking a ball, writing, cleaning the car and so on.

Sometimes your child may find it difficult to think in this way, so if you remember to reflect what you hear him telling you, you will acknowledge that you have heard and will avoid many frustrations.

Interestingly, many of the children at the Little School were largely children who had special needs and this is referred to later on. However, Alexander saw both the need and potential for the Alexander Technique within all schools and departments. Nowadays the Alexander Technique is taught within the music departments of some schools such as Oundle, St Paul's and Eton. It is also an integral part of the whole schooling at 'Educare'[13] the Kindergarten and Primary School in Kingston with ground breaking work by Alexander Technique teacher Sue Merry.[14] It is also part of the curriculum in music and drama colleges such as ArtsEd, RADA (Royal Academy of Dramatic Art) and the Royal College of Music (RCM).

Importance of breathing

'You know from experience that breathing can be interfered with by a wide range of things – psychological, emotional, mental, down to physical and muscular ...' Walter Carrington[15] – Alexander Technique teacher and teacher trainer

Curving over and curling up restrict free breathing. Your lungs occupy two thirds of the space in your trunk and nearly the whole of your trunk is active in breathing. FM Alexander was originally known as 'the breathing man' in Australia. He discovered that interference with the natural balance of the body then interfered with breathing and voice production. He never prescribed exercises as such for breathing. Instead he developed procedures to allow the breathing to work naturally and freely.

Alexander developed his technique because he realised the importance of postural support in breathing and reciting.

Breathing supports activity and communication. Frederick Husler (1889–1969), a singing teacher, coined the phrase 'Man is a Singing Animal' and indeed one can make sense of the idea that calling, whooping, shouting and all the vocalizing we are capable of stimulates muscular support and enhances postural tone.[16]

A properly supported voice is resonant and clear and involves the use of the whole body. Professional singers build up good body tone and are often very strong. Have you noticed how loud children's voices can be? They can run around shouting for hours! Where do they get all that breath?

Most people believe that in order to breathe in, you have to take a deliberate breath. We are taught, in class singing and in choirs, in playing any wind instrument: 'Now take a big breath'.

If we say 'No!' and instead *breathe out* then release the abdominal muscles, air will return. However, your Alexander Directions have to be working to provide the postural support needed for the right thing to do itself easily.

Many children get restless, fidgety and are unable to remain calmly still. If you have a bottle of soap bubble mixture and ask them to blow out really slowly, a bigger bubble can be blown through the ring. Really slow and gentle blowing may produce an enormous bubble. If you blow harder and faster, you will get lots of little bubbles. As children get older, they can learn how to control their out breath. They can blow more gently and sustain the flow of air for longer. This is calming and settling for the nervous system. Remind them to let the air come back easily without gasping.

A calmer deeper breathing pattern will help your child in singing or playing any wind instrument.

The back and limbs

In anatomy books one can see drawings of the perfect symmetry of the back muscles branching out to connect the arms and legs into the body. These muscles are woven together, sometimes in plaits, sometimes feeding in between the ribs. The main impression one gets is of a seamless garment clothing the bones, elastic in its nature and very strong. Arms and legs are very much part of this wonderful garment and derive their strength from being so thoroughly connected into the back. Your back extends from the lower part of your skull, at earlobe level, down to your buttock muscles.

We really don't have to think about how we reach for a cup of coffee, or bend to tie shoelaces – the brain and the body cooperate to bring about the desired action without specific planning – until, that is, we feel pain. All of a sudden we discover that even small movements can involve the back and cause a twinge. It's good to recognise that the back is involved in all activity.

Gravity and levity

'Gravity is gregarious, unstoppable, nosey: it reaches through your clothes to pull on your underwear, even tugs on time. Levity (once considered gravity's physical counterpart) is the lift behind flying, laughing, dancing, leaping' Emily Levine – American humorist

Let's look at gravity in this way: gravity weighs us down. Any buckling of the human support system will cause the body to topple and fall. Many people rely on this aspect of gravity to sit in an armchair! Make sure the chair is behind you, let your knees buckle and down you fall into it. Bump!

If the force of gravity causes everything to fall towards the earth, why do plants grow upwards, even without light? Plants use gravity to know where up is and where down is – so shoots grow upwards and the roots go downwards. Humans know up from down because of a complex organ in the inner ear that senses gravity's pull and signals the brain, keeping us upright. In standing still, the brain inhibits forward, backward and lateral movements once they are perceived. Measurements have shown that these movements are more exaggerated in people with tense necks. The brain is slower to pick up the movement signals. Once a decision has been made to move forward, the brain removes the inhibitory signal in the forward direction and gives permission for balance to change. The body falls forward under the influence of gravity, but responds to the postural reflexes taking it up off gravity. Thus you initiate movement by release towards gravity, which is immediately translated into levity, by the innate springiness of the muscular system.

As in the quote above: 'Levity – the lift behind flying, laughing, dancing, leaping', is wonderful! That's what the Alexander Technique provides.

We are levitators! Let gravity release you! Then move with levity!

Biomechanical efficiency

We hear a lot about how sports shoes will provide 'biomechanical efficiency' and change a runner's style. This approach could be called the outside-in approach. In order to change the impact on the runner's body of his foot hitting the ground, the shoe is designed to minimise this impact in precisely the area that gets the most force. After about a year, the shoe has become broken down and needs to be replaced. However, the runner's habits of movement causing the impact remain unchanged.

The Alexander Technique works from inside-out. First change the runner's habitual postural style, then the running technique will change and the impact on the body will be vastly alleviated. No new shoes needed!

In his advice on changing running technique, Roy Palmer, Alexander Technique teacher, draws attention to addressing the runner's concept of movement with what he calls body knowledge. *'This involves learning how to move with less effort by reducing the resistance many unknowingly bring to their running.'*

It's not only running which deserves attention and requires body knowledge. Nearly everybody unknowingly brings resistance to movement – resistance to walking upstairs, to getting up, sitting down, walking about, breathing, speaking, moving the head, gardening, reading – there is an unending list of activities to which we bring resistance, unknowingly.

Alexander himself addressed the question of biomechanical efficiency in everyday actions and tasks. For instance, when bending to pick something up, do you reach down with your hands, and pull the body after, rounding your back and keeping your legs straight? This is biomechanically inefficient.

The 'efficient' way to lift anything, as I'm sure you know, is to bend your knees, keeping your back straight. But Alexander realised that the idea that we can arrange the different parts of the muscular-skeletal system correctly at will (back, legs and so on) was simply not right. The muscular system must be co-ordinated as a whole and this co-ordination is critical in any action.

Muscular elasticity

'Understanding the total working of the muscular system, then, is a key element in solving particular kinds of tension-related problems and shifts the focus away from specific treatment of symptoms'
Dr Theodore Dimon [17] – Alexander Technique teacher and author

If we over tense our muscles to hold all the different parts of the body together, to hold the body up and then to move it around, we will set up awkward and strained movement through the increase of muscular effort. Muscular elasticity is lost in these conditions and a state of tension replaces elasticity as the basic norm.

Instead, we need to remember that the body has evolved to support itself against gravity. This natural support is extremely complex, involving neuromuscular activity throughout the entire body. Why complicate it more by imposing extra tension? Let the body's wisdom decide what support is appropriate against the pull of gravity.

If you observe an adult beginning to stand up out of a chair you will notice that, for most of them, the movement starts with an alteration in the position of that person's head. Instead of the head leading the body out of the chair, which is the way a small child would move from a squatting position to standing, the movement begins with the adult tightening the neck, pulling the head back and down and sticking the chin out. This is followed by an increase in tension in his trunk and legs to drive upward movement against the downward pressure of the head's weight on the top of the spine.

This is an example of a person imposing extra tension where it is not needed. Looked at logically, why would you want to add extra difficulties and force the spine down at the same time as trying to lift it up?

This unnatural way of moving continues through life, causes much tension and has an increasing impact as the person grows older.

However, it is possible to reverse the tendency to pull the head back and down if the person first stops and adjusts the balance of his head, to allow the head to balance freely on top of the spine. This has to happen in such a way that the muscles at the back of the neck will lengthen rather than shorten. The back and trunk will respond by lengthening, thus improving the overall quality of the movement and reducing strain.

How it all goes wrong

Why has it gone wrong? If you put your back out, you are likely to blame the last activity: 'It was that heavy case' 'It was lifting the baby into the car seat'. The expression 'it was the last straw that broke the camel's back' sums it up – all those years of piling on more and more weight and pressure on to the back through needless extra tension and compression. If you shorten as you tie your shoelaces, you will limit your breathing, tighten your abdominal muscles, shorten your neck and compress your body downwards onto your legs. When you get up again, that shortening will remain to do more damage another day. Your children are likely to pick up these habits too.

So what are you to do when you have had a stressful morning and find you have shortened and contracted your spine and are feeling tense and out of alignment? What you can do is to provide an opportunity to reset and restore yourself.

6. Reset and restore

'Rarely do people manage to stop and quiet themselves and get themselves into a situation of non-doing' Walter Carrington [18] – Alexander Technique teacher and teacher trainer

Many people rely on sleep to reset their over-stimulated systems back to the 'factory default'. Some need alcohol or smoking as well, to slow the brain and calm the nerves. These options are not appropriate for children, so bath time and story time is the moment to slow the day and wind down. I suggest you instigate other times in the day when everyone resets their system back to their 'factory default', perhaps the moment when you get home and before you get started on anything else.

Getting into the car before journeys, make time (a minute of silence, for instance) to become aware of anything you may have forgotten. As the rush and hurry die down, the brain has a chance to take stock, and often forgotten items come to mind. This could be something you do regularly each time you get into the car.

Also take time to calm down at mealtimes. Introduce the idea of one-minute silence while you and the children listen to all the sounds around and see how many you can count.

Releasing the spine

Time spent in the upright position, particularly in tense tight bodies, compresses the spine compacting the inter-vertebral discs. A study of children under five years old showed that they lost an average of two centimetres in height throughout their school day.[19] This is such a young age for compression of the spine. Other studies have shown that this shrinkage of the discs was reversed after 20 minutes lying down.[20,21]

The Alexander Technique recommendation is to spend twenty minutes lying down, which helps us to release the unnecessary compression of the spine and gives an opportunity for the inter-vertebral discs to expand again. It's good to encourage your children to lie down regularly.

Lying down the Alexander way

Find a comfortable and warm place to lie down on your back. The surface under you needs to be firm rather than soft so a carpeted floor is best. Carry with you a small pile of books which you will put under your head. The height of books is judged according to the normal positioning of your head relative to your shoulder blades. If you stand with your back against a wall, you will find that the back of your head doesn't touch the wall unless you force it to. This is the normal position I am referring to. That position will be between one and four inches, depending on your size and alignment. This is the height at which you need to support your head while you are lying down.

Once on your back, with the books under your head (remember that children, being small and slim, may only need one or an open book), bend your knees, feet on the floor close to your buttocks, and place your arms by your sides, or your hands on your tummy.

Begin to relax and allow your body to release towards the floor and expand over the surface, like jam spreading on a plate.

Without realising, we can keep our bodies stiff and unyielding while active. Once on the floor it takes time for muscles to unlock and release. Twenty minutes is the ideal length of time for adults, and maybe less, say fifteen minutes, for children. You could read to them or let them listen to a story to encourage them to stay lying still for this long.

Keep your breathing regular and easy. Listen to relaxing music if that helps, or, if your mind keeps revolving around to-do lists and worries, keep pen and paper handy, jot down reminders and then banish them from your mind. Don't answer the telephone and disturb this special time for you.

Getting your breathing going

This is also a good time to focus on letting your breathing deepen.

Remember that breathing out is the active part of breathing and that breathing in is passive – it is allowed to happen. Deliberately blow or breathe out and then relax: air will return. Widen your nostrils and open your throat (smile with the back of your mouth) so that air can rush back in easily. Now blow again, as if you are blowing out candles on a birthday cake. Relax and let the air return.

Whispering

Once you are used to this idea, you can vary what you do with your out-breath. Try whispering numbers, starting at one and stopping and closing your mouth when there is no breath left. "One, two, three, four, five" etc. Let the air return through your nose and start again at number one. This time you may find that you are able to count higher. Remember it is an unforced whisper, counting as many numbers as you have breath for, and returning to one next time. You will find your breathing deepens and you can reach higher numbers more easily. Eventually, unless you are very competitive, you will run out of breath at roughly the same number each time. Keep this up for a few minutes, then when you decide to stop, leave your breathing deep and even.

A vocal exercise that Alexander introduced was also whispered. It came to be called the 'Whispered Ah'. Using the same principle of not taking a deliberate breath to begin, open your mouth and, in a light sustained whisper, say 'aaaah'. Let breath return when it is all used up and begin again. Alexander recommended this exercise to prepare the voice for speech. His instructions were to place the tongue tip at the top of the lower teeth, think of something funny and let the jaw fall open very loosely to begin whispering a sustained 'aaaaah'. Close the mouth, let air return through the nose. Begin again.

It's a clever exercise once you know what you are listening for. The sound should be resonant but not forced, neither squashed nor silent. You can tell by the sound whether you are pulling your tongue back into your throat or squeezing in your vocal folds. Thinking of something funny widens the inside of your throat and releases your face and the sound acquires more depth and resonance.

Silence

So many people are alarmed by silence. Our culture is overloaded with auditory and visual stimulation. Signs beckon us to examine cut-price deals, every shop has 'muzak' to keep customers happy, loudspeakers announce the next train, flight, or the 'Tuesday shopping experience'. Traffic noise, aircraft noise, the noise of electronic devices humming away, televisions, sirens, lorries reversing and the thumping of personal MP3 players. Every kind of noise assails our ears for most of the day. However, if you really listen, you can observe other qualities: pitch, frequency, volume, variation. Lying down the Alexander way gives you the time to stop and experience a calm silence.

Hearing

If you are lying in silence, open your ears to the sounds around you, not only the near ones, but the ones in the background too. How many can you count? What quality do they have? High? Low? Sudden? Intermittent? Droning? Sweet?

Seeing

'Look at the colour of those bricks.' 'It's red,' I said, seeing it that way. 'Have another look,' said my father, pushing his hat further back on his head. As I looked again the solid red dissolved and now the bricks were many different colours; some were almost blue, or grey, or mauve, or pink or sandy-yellow. Only a few were brick red. Revelation! The colours came out at me, subtle in their differences, exciting in their unfamiliarity. From that moment I saw more than primary colours. The discovery was that the colours had been there to be found all the time' Joyce Grenfell [22] – English actress, comedienne and songwriter

Take a moment to look around you, even though you may be looking at the ceiling! If you are, take your eyes around the edges of any objects hanging from the ceiling – yes even the spider's webs! Let your eyes travel along the corner between the wall and the ceiling, the corners of walls, the shadows caused by light from the windows. Even boring details can become interesting if you look in this way. Become observant of variations in colours, light and shade. Imagine you are about to paint the scene. What colours would you choose for what you see in front of you? What shapes? How would you shade the objects that you see? Look for colours you think you can't see. It's surprising how often you will discover a colour akin to the one you are seeking.

Feeling

Before you get up, feel your body on the floor. Feel the contact of your back and feet against the surface of the floor. Where do you have the most pressure, where does your body feel lightest? Has your breathing deepened and slowed? What movements can you detect? Can you feel your heartbeat, the rumbling of your stomach, the clothes on your skin? In the same way as you observe your hearing and your vision, you can observe the way your body moves – your kinaesthesia.

Getting up

Roll over slowly onto your side. Take your time and keep breathing. Now push yourself up slowly and gently into a sitting position, then a kneeling position, then into standing. Stand tall and calm, remember to allow air to enter through your open nostrils and throat before breathing out again. Go a little more slowly than normal back in your daily life. Aim to float through the next activity.

Take these twenty-minute breaks once a day. They will save a lot of wear and tear.

Waiting time

There are those days when everything seems to get in your way or go wrong. The computer takes time to boot, you wait, tapping your fingers in impatience, or rush around busily opening your post. There are several people in front of you at the supermarket till, you shift from foot to foot, sighing, willing them all to hurry up. Your daughter has forgotten her trainers, the engine is running, she is late for school. On bad days you shout, offend your colleagues or sit fuming about everyone else's inadequacies, unable to concentrate.

You can turn this downward spiral of tension and stress around. Instead of getting frustrated and impatient, regard time when you have to wait as a blessing especially for you. Now you have time to give your Alexander Directions, to lighten up, to receive your fair share of air and refreshment and space. You will be in better shape for the rest of your day, and who knows, that cycle of aggravation may no longer be perpetuated.

Associate the action of filling the kettle and switching it on with breathing, lightness and poise. Watch the water swirling into your mug and notice the way it captures the light. Smell the fragrance of your tea or coffee, staying in the present. Leave the past behind and the future unanticipated, just for a few moments. Advertisements tell you that the drink must be a particular brand, but what they are really showing is the moment where senses return to the present and time expands. That moment isn't owned by a manufacturer, it is freely available and depends on your presence of mind.

Over involvement

When you get used to resting in your waiting time (for the traffic lights to turn green for instance), you will begin to realize how over involved you are in many situations. The stress of the last action gets carried over to the next, compounding the impact, making you tighter and tighter. Is it any surprise if you sometimes develop a headache, or that niggling pain becomes unbearable?

Pausing, returning to your balance and your Alexander Directions, freeing your breathing and your neck, cancels out the accumulation of self-inflicted tension and helps return you to a neutral state.

Pass through neutral

Your children need a chance to return to neutral too. With your imagination, you can develop a game of 'Start Over'; perhaps have a secret code that only the family understands. As I put my imagination to it now, the image of driving comes to mind. Neutral is the space in between gears and to which the gear stick returns when the car is idling. Each time that you change gear, you pass through neutral. I can imagine hearing the engine's revs and knowing when to change gear, moving to lower revs as I go faster and save on wear and tear. When your children are getting very worked up and excited, try calling "Change Gear, Pass through neutral! Lower revs! Coast!" Once explained and established, this could be a coded way of reducing stress and over involvement.

7. Putting it into practice

'We already notice, with growing amazement, very striking improvements in such diverse things as high blood pressure, breathing, depth of sleep, overall cheerfulness and mental alertness, resilience against outside pressures and a refined skill in playing a stringed instrument' Professor Nikolaas Tinbergen – Nobel Prize Winning Speech, talking about his family having had Alexander lessons

Listening and communicating

I have had to learn to listen to my children. I have had to learn how to communicate with them so that I was hearing their underlying messages. I have found books such as 'How to talk so kids will listen and how to listen so kids will talk'[23] and courses on 'Parent Effectiveness Training'[24] enormously helpful. The basic message is to learn to decode what your children are trying to tell you under the complaint that 'such and such was unfair' or 'their teacher was so mean'. These books talk of really hearing the coded message, seeing the state of agitation or unease in another person, and being true at the same time to your own feelings. They teach you to communicate so that you are heard whilst at the same time communicating what you are hearing and seeing in the other person.

I have found these teachings to be an extension of Alexander's ideas to the field of human relationships.

Listening, looking and feeling. We come back to it again in a new dimension. In this context, you listen to the tone of your child's voice, you look at their body language, you appreciate your own and your children's feelings and come into your own balance to steady them in acknowledging themselves. Children are often trying to tell you that they feel they haven't been listened to. You can alleviate their feelings of frustration by acknowledging their point of view. You can also ask them questions that stimulate them to think of the other person's point of view as well.

Of course, with babies, they can't speak and say what they want. There may come a very difficult time when your baby needs something, but you are unable to find out what the crying is about. There is a breakdown of communication! While babies are learning how to talk and communicate their needs, it is immensely helpful to have an in-between stage of communication. I heartily recommend a method of baby signing, which you can learn in a parent and toddler class. You and your baby learn songs with hand signals for the everyday events in a child's life: drink, sleep, milk, nappy, where? Mummy, cow, more, cake, rain – all of these make communication much easier.

In this way you will, right from the beginning, include your child in your life. A constant conversation develops between you and your child. Children are naturally very communicative. They become frustrated when what they have observed and what they want to tell you is ignored by you because you are too busy, or your mind is occupied elsewhere. Include your children, even when there is housework, cooking and shopping to do, by giving them simple tasks, like putting things away or finding something on the supermarket shelf. Don't worry if everything ends up in the wrong place! Actually, it's less time consuming to put everything in its right place, than to sort out a toddler who is throwing a tantrum because you have ignored her. Being inclusive and communicating well are two ways you can smooth out the day-to-day management of young children.

Letting be

The boys were fighting. Serious stuff, wrestling with all their strength to be the winner. They knocked over the table lamp in their struggle for supremacy. Aged eight and ten, they were about the same size, weight and strength. I quickly checked the room for dangers to their safety and stood in the doorway, an unwilling referee. I knew I had to let them have this fight. They'd been spoiling for it for ages. It was important for them to establish who was stronger and they were taking it very seriously. I longed to intervene, to have them be friends and play together as they had always done so harmoniously. But I stood and watched for their safety. The fight drew to a close, neither of them conceding victory. I made them shake hands to acknowledge that it had been a fair fight and then sent them off to their rooms to cool off and calm down.

I wouldn't have been able to let my boys have their fight if I hadn't trained in the Alexander Technique. I know I would have gone in there, got involved, made it my fight too. I would have ordered them around, been upset, added to the tension, blamed myself and given everyone a hard time. They would not have had that chance to learn respect for each other. I realize now that in standing by without interfering, I showed respect for them too.

Your 'awareness training' requires attention, first in obvious and tangible ways. Progress is made – starting with lying down for twenty minutes – and then progressing to waiting moments when you turn your attention to how light and open you can be in quieter times. This is followed by a more general awareness of what's really going on around you as you stay centred – identifying whether your immediate involvement is appropriate or not and what response you can make that is most helpful. Lastly, focus on what is going well and avoid reinforcing negative patterns.

The psychology of positive reinforcement is to encourage behaviour you approve of by making good behaviour a positive and enjoyable experience for children. Bad behaviour doesn't get the same attention and so lacks reinforcement even when it is used to get attention.

Keeping promises

Children need to regard the adults in their world as trustworthy so that they can learn for themselves how to be trustworthy. Keeping promises to children is of vital importance. The trouble is that as parents, you have to think on your feet about how to manage every situation, without having time to think carefully about how best to do this.

Your toddler is throwing a massive tantrum in the supermarket or your teenage daughter wants to go to a club with some friends this evening, giving you half an hour's notice.

In these situations some general points might be helpful:

- Set up general behavioural guidelines and agree them with your children well in advance
- Explain the reasons behind your decisions – their safety, their co-operation, your feelings
- Avoid threatening bad behaviour with consequences you are unlikely to be able to carry out
- Wait to breathe before responding
- Don't say no, then get fed up and say yes because it makes life easier
- Always follow up and carry out what you promise to do
- Agree with your partner that you will not countermand each other – otherwise the children will set you up against each other. Discuss any issues in private.
- Keep the lines of communication open
- Be clear with relatives what the family rules are and announce them when not under pressure

Internal discipline

Discipline is a very unfashionable word. Actually, psycho-physical management skills help children to build their internal discipline of themselves. If you practice freeing your neck and sending your head forward and up in the Alexander way every time you encounter a difficulty in your relationships, you will demonstrate the ability to stay calm under pressure. You will feel more capable, be better able to breathe, stand on your own two feet and know where your body is balanced in relation to the ground. It all comes back to Stop, Think, Act.

By communicating better within your own neuromuscular system, you will communicate balance to those around you. If you communicate well with your family they will learn not only how to communicate with you and others, but good internal communication skills too. They will learn to recognise much more objectively what is working well for them and where the interference is when they are not coping so well.

They will build more reliable sensory feedback because they will learn not to ignore their feelings, to acquire better judgement of where they are in relation to their surroundings and in relation to other people's feelings and attitudes. They will, in short, have better self awareness.

Sensitivity to touch

Holding a young baby is a very special feeling. They are so dependent, so trusting. There is no tension or fear. One's heart opens and fills with love. Make sure that all the physical expressions of your love for your child are accompanied by soft hands and a warm voice. They can be firm hands, just don't grip, tighten and tense up.

Of course this applies not only to holding your own baby; your partner, other children, parents, friends – all have occasion to have physical contact with you. The quality you hold in yourself, whether you are uptight, collapsed, heavy or nervous, is immediately communicated to anyone you touch. They will acquire a little of your quality from your touch.

When you give your child a hug, become aware of how you are breathing. Can you breathe more deeply and calmly? How are you holding your arms and shoulders? Could you relax them more? When you hold your sleeping baby, absorb some of your baby's relaxation. Notice how difficult it is to hold a screaming child. Try and relax your grip, soften the contact of your arms and body. This may help to calm the situation.

Now that you are making progress with allowing time, waiting time, time to notice the smell of your coffee or tea, the taste of your biscuit, try asking yourself the question 'How am I holding this mug?' Tightly or loosely? Can you loosen your fingers any more without spilling the drink? More still? When the mug is empty, put your other hand under it as a safeguard, and try slowly loosening your fingers until the mug actually begins to slip. Did you notice how your instinctive grip tightened to save the mug from falling? That will be the appropriate amount of tension in your fingers.

In daily life we are urged, again and again, to try hard, to do too much, to hold on too tight. We lack the confidence to believe that enough is just that; enough, sufficient. Please don't teach your children to do too much and hold on too tight! Like Dr Suzuki, observe how they learn, understand the stages of their development, be delighted at their success, however insignificant you feel it is!

Remember to go through neutral before changing gear, to travel faster on 'lower revs'. Use your Alexander thinking to put process before results. Your children will internalise this too when it's an established part of your rhythm.

Learning together

'I want to get old gracefully. I want to have good posture, I want to be healthy and be an example to my children' Sting – English musician, singer-songwriter

If you want your children to learn something, you will surround them with it. You will dance with your baby boy and teach him rhythm, you talk to your baby girl and she learns to speak, you sing and she sings. Children who have a parent who loves messing about with a ball will find that messing about with a ball is the best thing ever! Through your enthusiasm, they get their experience and skill at ball games. It depends how much time you spend doing these things with your children and fun you have with them. It also depends on how you teach them.

Dr Shiniki Suzuki observed how little children learn something as complicated as their mother tongue flawlessly. He noted that babies are immersed in language from birth. They are constantly encouraged by delighted smiles and approving laughter at every attempt. They progress by little steps and love to do what they can already do. He reasoned that they would also have the capability to learn anything if the method of teaching them follows what he called the 'mother tongue method'.

Start from the simplest action

Suzuki's method is enabling to children. It's a method that takes them from the very simplest action that they can already make, like pointing, to a similar action such as pointing a pencil, then pointing a violin bow. Very gradually the individual components of violin playing are built up until children become proficient, and progress through a graded system of musical pieces up to the very highest levels. What they can play at a very young age, and to a very high standard, is astonishing. Children who are learning the Suzuki method have high self-esteem and an amazing level of self-control. They obviously enjoy reaching standards of excellence and the discipline that it takes.

Obstacles never appear

It follows that every physical skill can be taught in such a way, whether it be football or ice-skating. What is important is that obstacles to learning these skills are removed, in fact they never appear. They are never allowed to impede progress.

How would you feel if you were handed a pair of tall stilts and then told, without any further preparation, to perform an action such as running with them on? You'd say, 'Come on, I can't do that!' All sorts of emotions would be present, many of them fearful and doubting. But if you know you are already able to run and then you learn to balance on tiny two inch high stilts, then to transfer your weight from one stilt to the other, you might acquire the confidence and skill eventually to run on tall stilts. Your success will depend on a gradual incremental learning process.

Keeping mind and body in step

'Movement is the door to learning' Paul Dennison – founder of the Educational Kinesiology Foundation

Our present culture is predominantly interested in mental skills. We place a great value on being intellectually active, to the detriment of our bodies. What is not generally taken into account is that body and mind are so completely interlinked that intelligence is developed and maintained most effectively with co-ordinated physical activity.

The Institute for the Achievement of Human Potential in Philadelphia has employed this understanding with their hot-housing of children. Their aim is to produce geniuses. The focus of the teaching is to speed up the developmental processes with intensive management of physical and mental stimuli.

This hot-housing programme of creeping, crawling, and 'monkey skills', combined with repetition of facts is very effective indeed. It proves to me that the brain works better and faster if mental learning is accompanied by physically co-ordinated activity.

It is generally accepted that learning needs to be child-centred, so I question the long-term value of forcing development beyond its natural pace, particularly if the child is not begging for it. That said, there is no doubt that learning is greatly enhanced if it is combined with physical movement.

You can teach your children so much in the home environment, particularly pre-school children. There is the recognition of symbols as representing something tangible and real, such as a bus; there are names to be learned, counting and rhymes. It's so natural for a little child to count the stairs as she climbs them, so natural to emphasise a word with arm movements or a jump. You find yourself using sing-song sounds and beating out rhythm as you join in with them. This is a great way to integrate 'mental' and 'physical' in learning.

Learning accompanied by physical activity

'Educational Kinesiology', is a movement-based programme aimed at enabling children and adults to reach their maximum potential. It aims to draw out innate intelligence through natural movement experiences. Called 'Brain Gym', its programme of specific exercises precede and accompany learning, and develop cross lateral co-ordination in children.

Some Alexander teachers find the Brain Gym exercises very useful when working with children as these are said to specifically address improving concentration and stimulate the neural pathways in the brain. What these Alexander teachers add to Brain Gym is the knowledge of how to activate children's central co-ordination through freeing up the head and neck relationship, a vital part of the nervous system's functioning.

Alexander teachers would agree with the Brain Gym organisation that 'moving with intention leads to optimal learning'.[25] They might modify the statement to add 'stopping to choose how to move with intention leads to optimal learning'.

You can help your child develop positively by keeping mind and body learning in step. This is a good basis for developing and maintaining enhanced functioning. So remember to:

- Allow your baby to crawl – lots
- Let her find her own way into standing
- Protect her while she is balancing but let her work it out
- Let her climb
- Encourage physical balancing skills and activities
- Remind him to remain tall and floaty
- Allow him to take his time
- Establish family 'waiting times'
- Draw his attention to sights, sounds, tastes and touch
- Trust that results arrive when the process is sequential
- Keep yourself breathing
- Let your own neck be free
- Remind her to reduce effort
- Touch her with less force
- Teach him about bony landmarks
- Set time periods with computers and TV
- Don't do any activity in a fixed position for too long
- Continually remind him to Stop, Think, Act

8. Thinking in action

The daily round

Now you are ready to begin to put these ideas into practice in everyday life. As every movement you make conditions and shapes your body, the daily round is your practice ground.

Standing – the plumb line test

So many people stand either on one leg, hip thrust to the side, or with hips further forward than shoulders and head. Thrusting your hips forward removes the support of the lumbar spine from the upper body and the upper back has to curve to remain balanced. Automatically, your neck pokes forward and your chin is raised. Thrusting your hip to one side creates a sideways curvature in your spine – a scoliosis. Looking from the back, the body takes the shape of an S.

People with muscular and joint problems are then given strengthening exercises to pull the shoulders straight, pull the tummy in and to force the back upright, as the predominant attitude to posture and fitness assumes that the body is weak and needs to be strengthened. However, if one were to look at posture as an excess of tension causing spinal contortion, one would seek to lessen the excess where it is occurring and provide an alternative instruction to the body to maintain a released and lengthened state of being.

If you were to hang a thread with a weight on the end of it from your ear, the thread should pass through the middle of your shoulder, the middle of your hip, just behind your knee and just in front of your ankle. This is the plumb line test. If you look at people around you standing in queues, you will see that very few of them stand with their weight evenly on both feet and their body aligned and lengthened.

Walking

Few of us walk anywhere without the encumbrance of bags, satchels or haversacks. Children often lug enormously heavy weights around school because there are no secure lockers in which to leave the bulk of their books and sports kit. If you have to carry bags, try and ensure that you bear the weight symmetrically. When you lift the bags, remember to Stop, Think, Act, before you bend your knees! Then turn your attention to lifting yourself and the bags centrally, by directing your head to release forward-and-up. You send your back up and away from the ground and the bags come with you.

If you want to increase the speed of your walk, think of the surrounding landscape travelling past you quicker and lengthen your stride rather than rushing forwards. If you have no bags, move your arms quicker to increase the speed of your walk. When you want to walk slower, slow the rhythm of your arms. These indirect means of getting the results you want reduce wear and tear on your body.

How to hurry

Whether you are walking, running, driving the car or riding a bike, there's an art to hurrying. If you are in a real hurry, remember that intention is the key to performing all the necessary actions in the most efficient way. Here your intention should be to reduce all interferences with your speed. Quick doesn't equal stiff! Don't tighten your head down onto the top of your neck – release it upwards. Don't tighten your legs and arms – release the joints so that you use their maximum potential for momentum and spring off the back foot. Keep your breathing easy – it won't help you to become short of breath.

If you are driving, you need to be as aware and clear in your mind as you can be. Banish the worry, look and listen with calm concentration and alertness. You don't need to frown or over-grip the steering wheel.

Finally, accept that you can only travel as fast as you can travel, accept that you are going to be late. This will help you to become calm in the circumstances. Make haste slowly!

Lifting with leverage

When you bend to pick up something, the most efficient way will be to position your body in such a way that there is minimum strain on your back when taking the weight. Mechanically, your body can be lowered so that your hands reach the object you want to lift, by bending at your ankles, knees and hips. Your trunk leans forward at an appropriate angle and your spine stays lengthened. Look at your family and see who does this naturally and easily. If you have children aged three and under, you will see an excellent example of how to get it right. If you see straight legs and a bent spine, then you can be sure that this member of your family has lost the ease and naturalness of early childhood.

Housework

How do you vacuum the floor? By pulling yourself down, shortening, narrowing and holding your breath? I know I used to do this and I hated housework. I particularly disliked ironing because I was so uncomfortable stooping over the board. Then I changed the way I did it. I took the trouble to set up my ironing board at a window, turned on some music, fetched a chair and lowered the ironing board down to a comfortable height above my knees, and thought about how I was bending to sit. I have never disliked ironing since then.

I learned to dance with my vacuum cleaner, an old upright hoover: forward onto the front foot, back onto the back foot, turn ... The hoover did the cleaning, I moved myself and it around. Good partnership eh? There is a temptation, with the head of a cylinder cleaner to scrub the carpet. Make sure the brushes are retracted so that the head can glide over the carpet. Then all you have to do is move your arm to and fro, and your body around. Step from the front foot to the back and again onto the front.

Work surfaces

Try and set up the height at which you work to suit your own height. If you are sitting at a computer or laptop, raise or lower yourself so that your elbows are the same height as the keyboard. It is helpful when sitting for long periods to have your knees slightly lower than your hips, but if you are tall and the desk is low this would mean raising the desk. You could certainly raise your laptop on a box file and get a separate keyboard if you find yourself stooping over it. Adapt your work-space to suit you.

The same principle applies when you stand at kitchen worktops to prepare food. The worktop should be at about the height of your elbows. If the worktop is too high for you, your shoulders are likely to become tense, particularly if you have to put pressure on a knife. If it's too low you are likely to stoop. Washing up can be a killer for tall people. Of course worktops are a fixed height so you need to be aware and remember your mechanically advantageous position. You can bend your knees and lean forwards from your hips and not your waist, keeping yourself lengthened and widened. When cutting and chopping let the kitchen implement do the work for you! If you are slicing bread, you push and pull the bread knife, it does the work. Don't be tempted to get in on the act and tighten your stomach muscles. They are not needed for pushing and pulling the knife.

Sitting in an armchair

Furniture is supposedly designed for comfort. Easy chairs are squashy, the seat is very deep, and your sitting position is conditioned by the shape of the back of the chair. Advertisements show people practically lying down in chairs and sofas. It's supposed to be so comfortable and relaxing. It is relaxing for your back, but only your back. Your front stays in a state of tension, your neck has to work hard to maintain the uprightness of your head when the support of the base of your spine has been removed from under it.

Anatomically the correct way to sit at all times is on your sit-bones with your spine vertical and your head balanced. If you are leaning back resting, you should support your back and head so that your body can remain lengthened. The seat under you needs to be firm. I used to place a board under the squashy seat of our new and expensive sofa. Our friends laughed when I called it my bed of nails, but it was so much more comfortable.

Watching TV

When our children were school aged but not yet in their teens, we found that one hour of television excited their nervous systems so much that we had to send them out into the garden to play for another hour, to work off the adrenalin. Watch your children carefully and limit the stimulus of television if you notice over excitement in them. Some families keep the TV on constantly and ignore it. My view is that it adds another layer of distraction to filter out and results in a dulling of awareness. The same applies to the constant over exposure to music in public places, on personal players, and to the over stimulation of computer games, without corresponding physical outlet. It promotes internal busyness and external collapse.

How to be tired

When one is tired one is disinclined to exert oneself, and for good reason. The body's instinctive response is to conserve energy, producing various familiar symptoms of coldness and lethargy. Of course getting adequate sleep and frequent nourishment is very important, but so is conserving your physical energy in practical ways that reduce muscular stress.

Here are some ways in which you can manage your tiredness:

- Keep your body in alignment so that your bones support you with minimal muscular effort
- Breathe without restricting your air passages
- Allow your ribs and abdomen to release as you breathe in
- Slow the pace of your breathing and let the breath deepen

Recent research shows that many children are sleep deprived.[26] Experts agree that children aged between five and twelve need ten or eleven hours sleep a night, whereas they get on average nine and a half hours. When becoming teenagers their circadian rhythms change and they stay awake later into the night, but feel very groggy in the morning. Some colleges are even experimenting with delaying the start of the studying day to 10am, to accommodate teenager's changed sleep patterns and the reports are of improved grades and fewer instances of depression.

However if you still have to fit into an early school or work start and can get no increase in sleeping hours, you can help yourself and your children to realign your bodies when active, breathe more freely and support your backs when sitting in chairs. Keep yourself vertically over your sitting bones with the full length of your skeleton from hips to shoulder blades against the back of the chair. Sit on a relatively hard surface. If your sofa is very squashy, put a board or tray under the seat cushion and place cushions behind your shoulder blades to keep you vertical. Taking the suggested 20 minutes to lie down the Alexander way can do wonders to revitalise you.

Lying in bed

Sleep is so personal and individual preferences vary. All I need to say is that sleeping on your back or your side is preferable to sleeping on your front, which tends to strain your neck and hollow your back. Medical opinion about sleeping on a hard or a soft bed fluctuates as research studies focus on different aspects of comfort and support. If you sleep on your side, fill the gap between your ear and your shoulder blade with enough pillows for your size, if on your back, you will need fewer. Relax in an open position, not a contracted one. It is possible to change one's sleeping habits, but one has to keep waking up to do so!

The important thing is to get enough sleep. In modern society sleep deprivation is a common occurrence. Studies show that both mental and physical health suffers and many apparently unconnected problems such as obesity can be traced back to lack of sleep.[27] As a busy parent, you need to be rested and alert in order to be quick thinking and inventive enough to avert toddler and teenage tantrums, and to find solutions which will diffuse potentially explosive situations and guide your children wisely.

The quality of your sleep can be greatly enhanced when you pay attention to keeping your poise and the freedom of your breathing in your waking hours.

Dealing with stress

It has to be faced that there will be times of the day and times of the week when you feel stressed. Often there is simply too much to do, too many people to look after, deadlines that are too tight. Emotional stress and worry added to daily pressure can tip you over the edge into illness. Sometimes you can no longer contain your feelings of stress, and they explode into anger and recriminations.

The other common response is to bottle up your feelings, trying your best to control yourself, and this can lead to depression, anxiety and exhaustion. Counselling or psychotherapy can offer you an outlet. It is a relief to meet somebody sympathetic to talk to, someone who can help you see your problems in a new light.

- Take the opportunities you can to release stress and anger, in physical exercise, in creative pursuits, and in rest.
- Remember to lie down for twenty minutes in the Alexander lying down position and restore your breathing.
- Use waiting time to de-stress.
- Stay in the present without anticipating the next difficulty or challenge.
- Stop regretting the past, you can't change it now. It needs to be accepted, though you may well resolve to do better next time.
- Deal with small everyday needs and attend to your awareness while you are busy with them.
- Learn to stop holding on. This is the way to live in poise.

It will be such a help to your children if you can live more in the present and let go of physical, emotional and mental tension, even if you can only do this occasionally.

Integration – your mindset

Learning the Alexander Technique increases mental awareness. Your mindset is all-important in acquiring control of your posture and movement. If you hold a heavy attitude about yourself, your body will reflect this attitude and become heavy and down. Head, neck, shoulders and stomach will fall forwards and down. If you hold a tense attitude, your body will tend to become restricted: chin, shoulders, chest, and kneecaps will rise in anticipation of the next challenge to be overcome.

Both of these states represent the extremes of conditioning, either tending towards depression or tending towards anxiety. The ideal is to stay within the bounds of a neutral state as much of the time as possible and to return to it when the stimulus towards extreme states has passed.

Each time you return to a balanced state of mind and body, you make space for your real self to live more harmoniously and confidently. It returns you to restfulness and calm, it helps your energy remain flowing and steady.

Don't take your movement for granted

By returning to a balanced state, both mentally and physically, you will enable yourself to become aware of the quality of the way you move. Can you hear the sound of your heels striking the ground as you walk? Your foot should fall lightly as you step forward. Does your back ache when you stand for any length of time? This may indicate tension caused by the misalignment between your hips and upper back. Do you push your face towards what you are looking at? This will make your neck and shoulders tight and strained. All movement conditions posture. Rather than trying to change your posture, change the way you move.

Relax to be ready

So much tension is caused by anticipation of what is to come, whether it is the next comment someone will make, or where you're going next. As I said before, Alexander called the immediate and unthinking rush into action and reaction 'end-gaining'. The rush to do causes too much force to be used in any activity and in any emotional reaction. Force and pressure dominate quick and unthinking reactions and the result is stress and tension.

To avoid stress and tension becoming a permanent state, give up your need to hurry to get in there quickly and sort stuff out. Stand back a little and consider what the best way of tackling something might be. By taking a little time and paying attention to yourself, your body, movement, breathing, eyesight and hearing, your brain will be freer to make wise and appropriate decisions on how to gain your end. Stop, Think, Act.

Awareness and attention

The process of paying attention, increasing your own and your children's awareness of balance and freedom, pays dividends in lessening stress and improving posture. Change comes about through a willingness to change, and that requires attention and awareness of your general state of being. Are you being heavy, congested, stiff, floppy and unco-ordinated, or light and free and balanced? Only then can you derive all the benefit of your good intentions.

Children are learning about life continuously. They will be interested in receiving information from you about themselves. Different ways of reacting can help them feel more confident and secure, and give them more skill in sports and other interests. You can help them gain insights into the causes of their discomfort, clumsiness, moodiness, or lack of confidence and show them through your example and love how to improve their poise – mentally and physically.

Reminders for thinking in action

Reminders on how to balance:

- Balance of the nervous system starts with the head-neck-back relationship
- Breathing continues freely
- Weight is taken by bones, so align your body appropriately, starting with the poise of the head
- Muscles work better if they start lengthened, so pause to let them lengthen
- Stay alert to your surroundings

Reminders on how to stay flexible:

- Don't stiffen!
- Don't try to force your flexibility, allow release to happen
- Head release initiates the undoing of the neck, back and breathing

- Give extra time for letting go beyond your present limit of flexibility

Reminders on how to lift:

- Efficiency comes from the integrated use of the head, neck and back
- Stop and give your directions before lifting heavy objects
- Breathe out when bending, wait while you release to breathe in and breathe out again when lifting
- Place your feet wide enough away from each other to enhance support

9. School life

'It (the Alexander Technique) bears the same relation to education that education itself bears to all other human activities' Professor John Dewey – American philosopher, psychologist and educational reformer

We need to broaden our vision and our expectations of how children should study. When have we ever stopped studying? Taken in its widest sense, we started studying at birth and we will finish at death. We studied how to grasp and move, roll, crawl and walk; we studied words and language; we grew in experience of people and their reactions; we learned facts and formed concepts; we acquired skills. We grow in wisdom and strength, learn how to care for others, how to be responsible and organized. Study is part of living.

Somehow, the idea of studying has become much more limited than this broad picture of life-long learning. We tend to assume we only study to pass exams; that the process of studying and being studious is a mentally active state but a physically passive one. We associate study with tension and striving, furrowing our brows and holding our breath, bending low over the paper, gripping the pen, shortening our bodies and our sight. Often this state is perceived as doing our best and being seen to be doing our best. Holding this attitude is the most effective way to incorporate strain into all brainwork and, quite possibly, to ensure that we hate every minute of it! It also leads to injury and illness, the incorporated tension and compression increasing stress and nervousness. These habits persist long after the hours of studying are past and become the blueprint for future endeavour of every kind.

If instead, you attend to physical and mental balance and variety, the picture changes dramatically. If you incorporate poise into your study procedures, your brain can stay refreshed and lively. So, by staying balanced on your sitting bones, supported by the length of your spine, feet on the floor, alert in your eyes, allowing the breathing to be free you will maximize your potential for concentration and learning.

Eyes and looking

The action of the eyes is vital to studying effectively. With the common habits of slumping and tensing, the muscles of the eyes can hold unwarranted tension. There is an intimate link between neck tension and eye tension. It is possible to release eye tension by releasing the neck, preventing fixing or staring and by understanding better how the eyes function. Not all of us are blessed with good eyesight, however, we can minimise eyestrain while we work at computers or read and write.[28] Electronic devices are compelling and the virtual world can absorb one's attention to the exclusion of the 'real' world. Here are a few tips:

- Look away from your hand held device frequently. Your eyes will benefit from the increase in focal length
- Break up concentrated work by getting up and walking about
- Change your activity when you notice your brain getting tired, such as when you can't find the appropriate command in the menu bar
- In others, watch out for tense foreheads and strained expressions, and feed the information about what you see back to that person
- Take a break from computing and look out of the window, use soft eyes and remember to breathe
- Take your eyes from the screen, look up to the ceiling, look down at the floor, look each side without moving your head
- Close your eyes, putting your palms over them. Enjoy the dark restfulness
- Blink frequently
- Include and widen your peripheral vision

Wearing Glasses

Spectacles form a frame around what you see. The spectacle-wearer's experience is that what is within the frame is in focus and what is out of the frame is out of focus. In order to keep what you want to see in focus, you have to move your head and this interrupts the flow between brain, eyes and head. As a result, your eyes become fixed and your neck lacks the responsiveness that would normally be aided by feeling free to look sideways. It has a detrimental effect on your head-neck relationship and the whole psycho-physical organism suffers.

If we are short-sighted we become largely unaware of what we see unless we are concentrating. We often acquire the habit of peering, almost pushing our eyes forward to see better. Short-sighted (and long-sighted) people need to retrain they way they look and see with their glasses on.

Firstly, if you or your child needs a new pair of glasses, make sure that you choose frames that provide a big enough frame through which to see. The fashion for very narrow frames is passing, and larger glasses are now more acceptable.

Next, as much as possible, move your eyes to look up or to look to the side, and only let your head follow when the rims of the glasses impede your view. What you may find is that you briefly see two images before moving your head to look through the centre of the lenses.

As you move your head up to look up, release under the chin rather than pulling the back of your head down. You will find that there is an accompanying opening and release in your chest as you lengthen the front of your neck.

If you want to look down, think of an image of a swan dipping its beak into the water. The back of your head goes up as your eyes look down and the back of your neck lengthens. If you think in this way, you will 'keep your length', instead of dropping your whole neck down.

Computer use

Our neighbour's son used to come into our house and sit on the floor, looking up at the TV screen to play with James' Nintendo. It was interesting to notice the two boys' different ways of using a games console. Our son would kneel so that the screen was at eye level and kept a long, wide back while his friend would sit bent over with a tense neck. James understood better than his friend that intense excitement didn't necessarily mean having tense hunched shoulders and tightly gripping hands.

There is increasing concern amongst parents that children are harming themselves by spending hours at the computer, playing games and surfing the internet. Not only does their posture suffer enormously, but their eyes may become fixed from staring at a screen and they may become short-sighted early in life.

Research is now showing that headaches, back problems and lack of concentration are associated with excessive use of computers and hand held devices. Many parents already limit the amount of time their children spend in front of screens, however, almost half of the parents in the survey reported that their children spend two hours a day and a fifth of the parents counted up to four hours.[29]

My advice is that each hour at the television or computer should be balanced by one hour of physical activity outside. The images cause undue mental stimulation and that needs to be balanced by a corresponding physical release of the stress.

Naturally, there can be intense peer pressure for your children to conform to the latest trends. When you allow computer and games use, you can also raise their awareness of their posture. It helps to provide suitably sized furniture which allows them to sit in a balanced way.

Writing

Writing requires poise. The fine tuning between brain and fingers works best when the neck is free, the eyes are lively, the back is upright and supported, and the feet are flat on the floor. Early in school life, if poor writing habits are allowed to go uncorrected, the body is slumped over the desk, eyes too near the work, breathing is impaired, and the spinal curves are exaggerated. Alexander teachers call this sort of posture 'pulling down'.

In pulling down the breathing and digestive mechanisms all get squashed and excessive muscular tension has to be used to stop us collapsing on to the desk! This affects writing ability hugely. The arm, wrist and hand are not able to move freely and despite our best attempts we struggle to produce neat flowing handwriting.

Educational Kinesiology, mentioned earlier, also teaches certain exercises to overcome overstress. One of these, 'lazy eights', is very useful in freeing up the arms and hands for writing. You begin to draw a figure of eight on its side on a piece of paper, circling round the left hand curve, then round the right hand curve, like tracing the outline of a pair of glasses without taking your pen from the page. Up and round, down and round, cross the middle line, up and round, cross the middle line, then down and round again. It is wonderfully calming, good for the brain and good for writing.

To write well, you should be sitting upright, balanced and free, both feet on the floor, remembering your bony landmarks for the support of your weight. Hold the pen lightly. No whitened skin due to pressure! Push the pen away from your palm to make upward strokes, and pull the pen towards your palm to make downward strokes. Sideways movements are made by moving the hand at the wrist. Writing along the page is accommodated by the widening of the upper arm away from the body before returning to its close position for the next line. Can you see the imprint of your writing on the next sheet of paper? If you can, you are pressing too hard.

Let the pen do the writing, you don't have to tighten your fingers, press harder, bend down low over the page, or hold your breath! All you do is to move it around.

Concentration and learning

In our culture, with its emphasis on mentality, one is led to expect to be able to do mental work for hours at a stretch. However, it's natural to get tired after doing the same thing for hours. One runs out of that particular kind of energy and needs to change the focus of one's attention.

Mental work is no exception, but there is a difference between creative thinking and organisational thinking. Decision-making takes a different sort of energy from the other two. You can vary your mental tasks during the day in order to keep fresh and alert.

Research has shown that the optimum time for sustained attention is twenty minutes and the maximum average time for focused attention is eight seconds.[30] If you take this into account, you can manage your workload, whether it be study or business, so that you maximize your mental capacity.

The best sustained concentration levels throughout the day are achieved by taking 10 minute breaks every 50 minutes. The school day is organised into forty-minute class periods, out of which teachers only expect to command sustained attention from children for twenty of those forty minutes. Don't expect more from your children at home without letting them take breaks to change their activity.

Here are some tips to help your family concentrate:

- Encourage them to sit in a balanced way
- Watch out for tensed foreheads and strained expressions and remind them to let go of the frown
- Intersperse mental activity with practical activity
- Draw ideas in a mind-map,[31] especially when the mind feels over loaded
- Read with rhythmical movements of the eyes, using a guiding finger if necessary
- When listening to music, occasionally turn it off and listen to the sounds around you, or listen to a different genre for a while. This refreshes your attention

Memory

Misusing your body directs energy away from the mind and impairs memory. As your co-ordination improves, your mind will be less cluttered and more focused. In line with the present day interest in the brain and in mental skills, there are some useful avenues of research on learning methods. These approaches advocate relaxed awareness, mind calming, and knowing yourself and the way you learn. As the Alexander Technique is renowned for improving relaxed awareness and calming the mind, it is highly appropriate for improving memory.

Here are some guidelines for improving memory:

- Memory improves when sensory input is greater. Link the subject with different sensory inputs, i.e. reading aloud, listening, watching, acting out and making models.
- Repeat positive experiences
- Break learning down to steps that are manageable
- Four-second sound-bites are the most effective for learning facts
- The brain is most retentive when very relaxed and dreamy
- Make sense of what the subject is about
- Look at the big picture and put the details into context

Exams

Once the exam time has arrived, no more can be done to prepare. It is time to perform. To be ready for any performance, one needs to be calm, poised and well prepared, confident that one will do one's best and accepting that one can do no more.

Preparation for exams needs to be started in plenty of time. Teenagers easily collapse into inertia and procrastination. Too often, children will put off beginning revision and preparation exercises until they are in a panic. Realism is the key here, and acceptance of the limitations of the situation. There will never be enough time for the hard workers to feel that they have done enough, so they need to accept what will be just enough and what will not be enough as well as visualizing what would be ideal.

Here are some ideas on how to manage the planning:

- Decide on priorities
- Be realistic over timing and attention. Good intentions are all very well, but how realistic are they? Do they have enough minutes to do all they plan?
- Allow for interruptions. Give extra time for changing subject. All transitions take time
- Plan in breaks, again, be realistic. Plan in 'rewards' and feeling good

- Start with modest plans - they can always do more if feeling buoyant and pleased with themselves
- Plan a whole week at a time of homework and revision. Take a long hard look at the possibilities of not achieving all the targets and have a plan B (and C) in place
- The focus of the planning is to avoid rush and panic and to maintain a calm and orderly pace

If, during the exam, you find you are becoming confused, dazed, or have too many thoughts and cannot get them in order, Stop. Then begin forming lazy eights on a spare piece of paper. Carry on with these until they become regular, even and fluid. This is a wonderful way of calming and ordering the mind.

Sport and fitness

In general

This is not the place to give exhaustive details of how to achieve mastery in different sports. Any sport will be accomplished better if the athlete has good use rather than poor use of himself. A pillar of achieving excellence in sport lies in the postural education and mechanical understanding of the sportsman. This is best encouraged in early childhood, and prevented from deteriorating in teenage years by training in Alexander awareness, relaxation and directed attention.

The London 2012 Olympics wonderfully raised the level of enthusiasm and motivation in children and young people to become physically active and to participate in sport. 'Inspire a generation' is a worthy goal. But how do we best go about it?

Back in the 1950s, a study of the daily activities performed by children as part of school life was conducted by Jack Vinten Fenton, a headmaster of a secondary school and former physical education lecturer.[32] The study concluded that none of the activities performed were potentially strengthening, few of the activities were likely to improve mobility of the joints and approximately half of the activities might be likely to produce some degree of kyphosis, an undue curving of the upper back.

He introduced a preventative scheme into school, of developing good use of the body through directing the children's attention to the body as a whole, collecting themselves and checking over for tension and imbalances, before forming a clear intention of what to do next. He stated that 'good use of the body in many children is not spontaneous, it has to be taught'.

Vinten Fenton also observed that as posture and awareness improved, so did mental alertness and receptivity. He advocated that the training of teachers should include teaching children to become aware of their posture, and teach them how to relax and take a moment to consider that they have a choice of how to manage themselves in every activity, including study.

You might be thinking, 'What relevance has this got today? That was the 1950s'. A more recent attempt in 2010 to improve fitness, motivated by concern that P.E. in schools does not provide a sufficient workout, led to the British Association of Sport and Exercise Sciences recommending a five-minute fitness drill for children in school. The five-in-five routines involve squatting, lunging, pushing, bracing, rotating, and getting puffed out. Whilst the specific exercises are very commendable and vitally important, what is apparent in the videos showing the exercises is that the children's use of themselves remains poor. Without the basis of good use, they will fall short of the mark. Attention is paid to the activities without insight into how children actually achieve the routines. They exercise with hunched backs, shortened necks and general lack of balance. Their natural grace and symmetry has already been lost.

They need to be taught how to regain poise, recognising that a truly healthy body requires attention to posture and the whole movement pattern including the head and neck, rather than to specific exercising of individual parts of the muscular system. If the instructors were to attend to teaching the children first how to prevent undue tension and then how to form a clear intention of what they are aiming for, the resulting aligned posture and dynamic poise would enable them to carry out the routines efficiently and well. This applies to any fitness or sporting activity.

There is a general principle that should run through all sporting activity. The principle is 'the head leads and the body follows'. Remember that eyes lead all movement. This is apparent in animal movement: the eyes, nose and ears lead the animal's head, and the body follows. Look after the whole body's poise in order to make specific movements. At the same time, attend to the release needed in specific muscle groups in order to make a specific action, whether it be kicking or hitting a ball or practicing martial arts.

To achieve excellence in any sport, form is essential. Sports people study their form minutely. The better they become, the more they attend to the means of maintaining their form. Top athletes have to muster great discipline and determination, and have to lose all the impediments of personal style which interfere with their performance. They have to say 'no' to what they don't want, from their diet through to their everyday habits. The Alexander Technique can form part of this picture by practicing Stop, Think, Act.

By saying no to all the distractions, this opens up space and time, allowing the freedom and determination to win, to grow. Sportsmen and women should aim to achieve natural poise and the Alexander Technique can help them gain and maintain this, thus minimizing undue injury and maximizing longevity as an athlete. Health and fitness at these high levels can then be maintained better over a longer period. Mind and body can be in that inseparable state of dynamic poise called 'the zone'.

Fitness exercises

The modern emphasis on keeping fit is largely unchallenged. Fitness is seen as part of a healthy lifestyle, and because so few people have access to natural countryside or activities that take place in the country as a normal part of the day, their sedentary lifestyles lead to problems with their health and strength. Even children become obese if their natural energy flow is stagnant for much of the time. Health conscious people will be proactive in taking exercise by swimming, aerobics classes, running, or lifting weights with the help of a fitness instructor.

But the drive for fitness can become unbalanced and excessive. There is a danger that fitness is seen as a quality in itself, judged merely by body build, without much reference to how it should enhance physical, mental and emotional freedom as well as strength.

It is almost impossible to avoid exercising the bad habits that people bring to their fitness training - breath holding and blocking in the throat, contracting the chest, hollowing the back, tightening the neck, forcing upward movement with the legs - unless one has already built up postural awareness and an understanding how to lengthen and widen. Gyms are full of people causing themselves harm through the exercising of their postural shortening and narrowing.

Alexander teacher Malcolm Balk has explored this subject in his book 'Master the Art of Working Out'. He advocates treating exercising as an art rather than a science. In order to remain interested in the process, one must abandon the idea that exercising is a necessary evil. *'Such thinking can add exercise to the list of robotic mundane activities that characterise so much of our lives. When we cut our minds off from what we are doing and simply repeat movements over and over, in a mechanical fashion, without interest or curiosity, without thought and without intention, we reduce both the experience and ourselves in the process. After all, who needs to spend more time at the office?!'*

Running

Running is both a discipline in itself and a basic ingredient of many sports – football, rugby, hockey and netball to name a few. There are many methods of teaching running e.g. Pose Method, Barefoot Running, and Chi Running. The common factor is that they all rely on maximising efficiency and encouraging poise in the body. The Alexander Technique approach has been excellently covered in 'Master the Art of Running' by Malcolm Balk.

My advice on running is simple: Run up, not down. Aim your body off the ground, stay compact, move your hands forwards and backwards to control your speed, free your neck, lengthen and widen your back, sending your knees forward-and-away, and off you go.

Your weight should be landing over the balls of your feet rather than your heels. Notice if you can hear or feel your heel landing heavily. If you are, your weight is too far back. Bring it forward a tiny fraction until your footfall becomes lighter. Your body will feel more compact and you will move faster, with less resistance and impact on your joints. Maintain your upward length as you extend your stride and look out rather than down. Let your arms move freely and allow your forwards and backwards reach to balance your leg movement.

It may be helpful to time your breathing to your footfall. I suggest breathing out for twice the number of paces that you need to breathe in. To put it another way, breathing in should be quicker than breathing out. If you need three paces to breathe in, slow your out-breath to six paces. Try this and then vary the ratio of the timing of your in and out breaths to suit your stamina.

Above all, your aim should be to stay light and free, to reduce work rather than increase it and to replace the work with efficiency.

Recognising errors

What we are looking for here is not to recommend a certain running technique or style. Rather, it's to preserve efficient free body movement with good poise. Prevention is the key – stopping what we don't want to happen. The Alexander Technique helps us to know this for ourselves.

What *not* to do when running:

- Stick your jaw forwards
- Poke your neck forwards
- Bend backwards lifting your chest
- Take your weight back and hit the ground hard with your heels
- Bend down in a curve hunching your shoulders
- Keep your arms rigid and twist from your waist
- Lean back to slow down

How to recognise errors in your children's running:

- Listen to their breathing. Is it always laboured?
- Look out for head position. Do they stick their chins out?
- Are their shoulders raised?
- Do they land heavily on their feet?
- Do they lean back? Or overly far forward?
- Do their faces show tension?

When you have noticed one of these characteristics, try giving a gentle instruction to aim for the sky, or to fly more, or to 'oil' the movement more. Maybe talk about how animals move. Invite their observations and ideas. Invite them to copy animal movement: tortoises, cheetahs, elephants and so on. Ask them to demonstrate really heavy sticky movement or stiff breakable movement or wild rolling movement and then contrast it with something they feel is the opposite. Feed them with interesting tidbits of information such as 'did you know that your head weighs as much as two large bottles of coke?' Then you can suggest ideas like 'don't you think it would be good to have a cushion of air under that weight?' Show them where the head and neck meet. Get them to demonstrate what it would be like for them to run with the weight stuck down onto the top of the spine, then contrast it with having an imaginary cushion under the head, just level with the earlobes and the head floating on top.

There is much that you can do to help your children's freedom and ease of movement. You will need time with them, conversation with them, good observation, information about balance and use of the Alexander approach.

Music, dance and drama

We could apply the idea of fitness to musical prowess, dance or drama. One has to be supremely fit to apply the physical strength, balance and flexibility needed in each of these areas of interest. The ideal would be to start learning to play, dance or act from a clean slate of beautifully balanced use of the self, but that is a rare occurrence. If the child is well taught, poor co-ordination is spotted and eliminated by instruction that encourages the undoing of habitual tension patterns. However, teachers may easily take the patterns of poor use that they encounter as normal, and often the result of their exhortations to try harder to stand up straight increases the tension in their pupils, with long-term harmful results.

Musical performance

Playing a musical instrument is hugely demanding on co-ordination, and takes mental and emotional energy. Teamwork is also essential for music in groups. Calming the nervous system and fostering postural support, the Alexander Technique clears interference out of the way of good instrumental technique and musicianship. In singing, balance and flexibility throughout the whole body is vital for the power needed to project the voice.

If your son or daughter learns a musical instrument, you can help their practice be more productive, even if you know nothing about how to play the instrument they are learning. Maybe you could even consider learning the instrument alongside them, to give you more inside understanding of the difficulties they face. Would it be possible for you to attend a few of their lessons to get to know their teacher and what he or she is looking for?

Your primary consideration would be the development of good co-ordination and the avoidance of tension patterns associated with playing that instrument. Look for:

- Raised shoulders
- Braced legs or standing on one leg only
- Breath holding
- Facial constriction
- Head dropped down, or on one side
- Elbows sticking out

You can comment on how uncomfortable and tiring it is to hold tension in these places and does it really help their playing? You can ask them to experiment with walking around the room while they play (unless they play the cello or double bass or piano of course!). You could introduce them to a balance board and have them stand on it while playing. You can ask them to take their eyes from the music and look around, or notice movement in their peripheral vision while they concentrate. You can remind them to keep their shoulders smiling instead of frowning (this is a better instruction than 'relax your shoulders'). They should occasionally practice in front of a mirror to see themselves as others see them, or you could video them so that they can both see and hear themselves.

You will be helping them with their primary instrument, themselves, to provide the best conditions for learning the secondary instrument, the violin, trumpet, piano, voice, or whatever instrument they choose.

Dance

My son in law teaches ballroom dance. One day when his two year old son was tottering around the room, he remarked to me that he had changed how he teaches his ballroom dancers to move. 'See' he said 'I've been watching how Emrys does it. It's so simple, he lets his head fall forward and then his body falls towards the direction in which he is going. Now I tell my dance students to fall forwards, and it's brilliant, they move totally naturally.

Dancers train to be poised. Glenna Batson says: '*At the heart of a dancer's training lies the cultivation of muscular effort – its degree, sensibility, precision, refinement. ... [Dance] aficionados say that the Alexander Technique is "the technique under all techniques", because it is a process of embodied thinking, sensing, and acting. Through studying the Alexander Technique, dancers can move with greater ease, poise, and accomplishment, regardless of the movement style*'.[33]

If your teenage daughter learns ballet, she will maintain a recognisable dance posture through her daily life. Dancers hold their heads up high, stand tall and straight. However, there can be a tendency to over extend the body and narrow and shorten the back, particularly if the teacher tells the dancers to try hard to stand up straight. What is meant to look effortless begins to show signs of strain. When I learned ballroom dance, my teacher admitted to being a bad breather. She said it was difficult to breathe when you danced, particularly for ballroom, as the arms have to be held up high. This is only true if the way you hold up your arms is to tense your lower back and raise your chest, thus constricting your lower ribs – that part of the back which is vital in free breathing. The upper body can be freely raised for the correct ballroom position by releasing your stomach muscles and releasing at the top of your thighs.

I have found the idea that you must suffer for your art widely accepted, not only in the musical arena but in dance and sport also. Along with this assumption that you cannot be good unless you hurt, other assumptions are made: you must control certain parts of the body while isolating that limb or section of the torso from the rest of the body. The neck must be extended to the point of over-extension, the abdominals held in tightly and breathing forced against the strain of holding.

In their excellent book on 'Dance and the Alexander Technique',

Nettle-Fiol and Vanier look at dance through the lens of developmental movement.[34] In approaching it this way, they are enabled to approach the teaching of dance from an alternative point of view; considering the whole versus the parts, focusing on process rather than results, non-doing rather than doing, direct touch transmission rather than imitation, and overall co-ordination rather than trying to copy appearance of shape or form.

'This approach to one's self and one's training requires a radical shift in attitude. Instead of seeing the body as a static set of conditions to be positioned, corrected, tamed, and polished, we become a continually changing process of events, responses, and choices that may be observed, quieted, redirected, or left alone'.[35]

Lookout points for dance practice, particularly:

- Raised shoulders
- Raised chest, hollow back
- Breath holding
- Glazed eyes
- Braced legs

Remember your reminders to your child would be couched in positive language: 'smiley shoulders, generous breathing, lively eyes'.

Drama

Acting and using the voice is greatly enhanced by a basic condition of good use. This is where the Alexander Technique began. It was through trying to portray other characters that Alexander discovered his own limitations of vocal and physical use.

Acting is greatly limited by a person's restricted emotional and physical field. The school play can be an agony of hearing declamation with limited and repetitive vocal pitch and range. Children's stiff shoulders or habitual stoop can make a mockery of the portrayal of brash or exotic characters, conveying instead caution and lack of self-confidence.

We only realize how much an actor depends on body and breath to support a role when we see the shortcomings of those who are largely unaware of how to manage their bodies in a convincing way, or of how to manage their breath to support the voice. For many people who have to speak in public, projecting the voice seems an impossible task and they cannot be heard at the back of the hall. Voice projection requires strength and flexibility in the ribs and abdominal muscles. Habitual tension in the torso along with stiff legs prevents this flexibility and the voice fails to carry. Although good teaching can go some way to overcome these problems, until the underlying use is addressed by the Alexander Technique, the child will struggle to carry out the teacher's instructions and believe himself to lack talent.

Arts and crafts

It would be natural to assume that improved posture would hardly affect the end result of a drawing or painting – the artist either has the visual and manual talent or not. Art is seen as a restful and creative occupation that does not involve physical stress. But any habits of breath holding, stooping, stiffening, bracing, or undue tension that a person carries can cause discomfort and lead to fatigue. These habits of holding unnecessary tension also interfere with concentration and accuracy.

Art benefits children in so many ways. They acquire better hand/eye co-ordination and control. Through making, looking at and talking about their artwork and that of others, children can learn to express their feelings in a safe way. Their perceptions of colours, textures and shapes, and their growing expertise at handling implements can give them confidence, practice in making choices and solving problems. They learn to look and see differently. It is highly educative in a holistic way.

Craft, design and technology skills require strength and accuracy, and the body must be used properly to achieve a steady hand when bending over a lathe or workbench. The craft departments in schools are filled with boys and girls bending poorly over workbenches and lathes, working in positions of strain, with mechanical disadvantage over their implements. They need training in how to raise or lower their stance to achieve positions of ease as they work.

These detrimental habits of posture can go on to cause repeated back strain in adulthood. The loss of many working days is attributed to back strain and injury. The NHS quotes 9.3 million working days lost per year due to work related back pain and musculoskeletal disorders.[36] It is now the second most common cause of long-term illness in the UK. Although these statistics include office workers, government statistics on days lost to back pain due to manual handling quote 4.5 million. School and home are the places where children and young people should be taught how to manage their bodies without strain.

Special needs

Alexander believed it was important to incorporate his technique into the field of education to prevent problems and to improve learning at an early stage. In 1924, after he had worked successfully with a child with educational learning problems, some of his pupils asked to send their children to him for lessons. He then founded the "Little School" in London, helped by two of his assistants, Irene Tasker, who had been trained as a school teacher by Maria Montessori, and Margret Goldie who had trained at the Froebel Institute.[37] In the school, children were encouraged to maintain optimal co-ordination in their academic lessons as well as in all their other activities.

The children who attended the school were largely children for whom orthodox education would have been unsuitable, due to their special needs. It is clear from the pictures taken at the time that they took part in farming and household activities in addition to their schooling. They all look very happy and calm. There is evidence that the improvement in their overall balance and co-ordination improved their breathing and posture, and maintained good overall health.

A number of Alexander teachers have worked with children with special needs, among them Eileen Armstrong, who says 'as alignment improves, perception of the world can be more accurate. Mood can also be improved ...' Also STAT, the Society of Teachers of the Alexander Technique, says, 'Learning the Alexander Technique can help prevent or alleviate conditions associated with undue tension or poor posture.' This is equally true for people with learning disabilities. Their problems may include abnormal muscle tone resulting in movement difficulties and distorted body shape; inability to express need or deal with stress, which might present as behavioural problems; heavy reliance on habitual and stereotyped movement patterns which, although self-comforting, are very limiting. Helping your child with special needs with the Alexander Technique can help him gain poise and achieve his best.

10. The home environment

'Half of British children suffer from back pain due to slouch potato lifestyles' British Chiropractor Association Study 2008 [38]

You and your home are the biggest influence of all on your children's poise, confidence and happiness. The key word here is support. Your home should support you and your family's welfare by a wise choice of what you sit on, what you lie on, how you relax, how you accommodate your independence from each other and your togetherness too. This extends to what and how you eat and drink; making time and creating space away from the rush and hurry; finding opportunities to support each other as the ages of your children allow; in short, de-stressing, unwinding, being peaceful as well as excited, happy and interested.

Support and nourishment

It's not always easy to get enough sleep in a busy week and many children are measurably sleep deprived. Even if bedtime rules are strict, children may still not sleep until late in the evening. They can become 'wired' by watching stimulating programmes on TV, or playing games on their mobiles, posting messages on Facebook and sending texts. I recommend periods of exercise and fresh air in between periods of concentration and stillness. A guideline for younger children is to intersperse one hour of TV with one hour of outside activity. In these ways you can provide rhythm and structure to your children's lives.

There is another form of support that you will find very helpful, and that is emotional support.

As you apply Alexander Technique to your life, you will become increasingly aware of the effect of your choices in different areas, and the effect that these choices have on both you and your children. When people are completely unaware that they are constantly choosing how to react to circumstances and events, they put the blame for their illnesses and their moods on the external environment. 'It was that heavy case I picked up that put my back out'; 'that email ruined my day'; 'this kitchen drives me mad'; 'my teacher is stupid'. It takes more awareness to realise that it was their reaction to the email, how they bent to pick up the case, their feelings of frustration with the kitchen, the impression that the teacher wasn't listening, that contributed to the tension they are already carrying. If we can be more objective in our descriptions of events, the phrases would change to: 'I picked up that heavy case awkwardly and without preparation and put my back out'; 'I felt a great deal of anger and resentment over the email which I couldn't let go of during the day'; 'I feel very frustrated and tense when I work in this kitchen', 'my teacher keeps repeating the same things over and over'.

By recognising more accurately the source of any problem you can start to change your response. It gives you choice and that will give us power.

Once you get the hang of this new way of thinking, you can rephrase what you hear your children telling you and ask questions about what it feels like when they think their teacher is stupid. Their answers will give you more information and often a solution. But more importantly, it shows them that you are really listening and this is emotionally supportive.

When we stop blaming the external environment for our woes, we empower ourselves to make changes which will allow us to feel more supported and nourished.

Furniture

The Victorians knew a lot about furniture. At the height of the manufacturing era, they had the resources to invent furniture that supported them and made life easier and less arduous. Thus there were reading stands, bell pulls and arm chairs which protected the person from draughts and fitted the person using them. Not these days, when everything is mass-produced and furniture is designed for the 'average person' – a size that fits no-one. Train seats are notoriously uncomfortable for everyone. The design of seating is based on research that measures the curves of a person's back and then aims to support those curves. However, when you are considering the human frame as a vehicle for movement, different factors come into play. Does the seating support your bony landmarks? The best seating supports your sitting bones and your shoulder blades, because those are the parts of the body where your nerve endings respond to pressure and activate your postural reflexes.

Armchairs and sofas are often very deep seated, which suits the longer legged, but not shorter people. Pad out the back of your armchair with cushions if you have shorter legs. The eventual size of the seat of the chair should be the same length as the backs of your legs to the knee, unless you use a footrest. Remember to support your shoulder blades as well as your lumbar spine. If the seat reclines, put a cushion to support your head, otherwise your neck will tire.

School plastic stacking chairs are excellent ... for stacking, not for sitting in. The seat is rarely horizontal, and is instead higher at the front than at the back. The effect on the body is to tip weight back with the consequent effect that the pelvis rolls under. The child is then sitting, not on the sitting bones, but on the tailbone. It's no wonder their backs ache if they have to maintain this uncomfortable position for an hour or two. It's not surprising that children grow up expecting to sit with curved backs, because the seating compels them to do so. The only way to deal with such a chair is to sit right on the edge as if it were a stool.

Once you know how proper support helps your body respond appropriately, you are free to understand how to adapt furniture to fit you, and choose the right horizontal support for your child's size. Should the chair from the local toy store not have a horizontal seat, you can adapt the back legs with a small wedge to bring the level up. There is a make of children's chair called the Tripp Trapp chair. These wooden chairs can be enlarged as your baby grows into a toddler and older by lowering the foot platform. They even stack.

The point about taking care over getting the right seating is to establish good habits of sitting. You will inevitably experience the occasional uncomfortable and unsuitable chair, but you can take that in your stride, if your habitual expectations are that chairs and tables are there to fit you, not you to fit them. You can raise the height of your work table if you are tall, or sit on a higher seat and use a footrest if you are too small.

Parents of young children and babies spend a fortune on pushchairs and baby carriers that are chosen for their versatility. The law will not allow a child to travel in a car without being strapped in and so one is confined to the manufacturer's designs. Although much attention has been paid to the safety aspects of such seating, no thought appears to have been given to the impact that these seats will have on the infant's neuromuscular receptors and the longer term conditioning of its postural reflexes.

The most sensible attitude towards this is to limit the length of time you spend in the car, and the length of time your baby has to be strapped into a seat.

Carrying car seats is an awkward business, and leaning into cars to place the child in the seat, or the seat with the baby asleep in it, can be a strain on your back. Likewise putting pushchairs and shopping bags into the boot of the car, leaning over with a weight at arms length, takes a lot of strength. Here, applying the Alexander Technique would involve avoiding tipping your chin out and pulling your head back, as that increases pressure on your back, and, wherever possible, bending your knees as you lean forwards. Use momentum to help you swing the weight forwards, and get yourself as close as you can to the weight you are carrying. If you need to, break the whole manoeuvre into several stages of movement to move children, seats and bags from one place to another.

When you yourself sit in the car, have your seat reasonably upright. If it leans back very far, your neck has to adjust its angle to keep your head upright for you to be able to see ahead, and this can be a strain on your upper back and constrict your upper chest. Pad out any exaggerated seat hollow behind your shoulder blades. There will always be support for your lumbar spine as the 'myth of maintaining the lumbar curve' is firmly embedded in seat design. So modify its exaggerated effect by supporting your shoulder blades.

I encourage you to study your workstation and become aware of the relative heights of your computer keyboard and chair. It needs to fit you. Your hands should be slightly lower than elbow height, your knees slightly lower than your seat, the mouse not too far forward, and your telephone within easy reach. The top third of the computer screen should be slightly below eye height so that you are neither tempted to tip your head back, nor lean so far down that you slump.

Fashion

I observe that fashion values change every few decades. In the 1950s women's fashion displayed attitudes of compliance and grace. Women were portrayed demurely, knees together, ankles elegantly disposed, smiling invitingly. In 2012, women are portrayed raunchily, hips thrust forward aggressively, belligerence manifesting at every jerky movement. Mannequins are made with exaggeratedly bad posture – models' make up is chalky white with dark shadows under the eyes. Why are they modelling drug addiction? Is it that compulsion to taste forbidden fruit? Men are portrayed as unsmiling, dour, introverted. All this has a pervasive influence on our expectations of normality, and flies in the face of any image of natural poise.

How about you? Do you really want to portray these values? Have you the figure for it anyway? What about being natural, authentic and attractive?

Let's think about what the body requires. Most of all it needs freedom to bend and flex. Do your clothes allow you to bend at the hip joint or do they restrict the movement of your legs? Is your handbag very large and heavy? Are your shoes tight at the toe? Do they stay on your feet? Do the heels put strain on your lower back?

Food

As you begin to pay attention to looking after yourself in healthier and more balanced ways, you may come to the point of considering what you eat and how you eat. Just as the kinaesthetic sense of your posture can be misleading, your sense of taste can also be misleading. It will tell you what you are used to, not necessarily what is good for you at any given moment.

This is not the place to offer dietary advice, only to say that if you wish to change your eating habits, the Alexander Technique gives you a method: that of stopping and working out the means to achieve your desire whilst you maintain your poise. Sometimes all that is needed either to avoid eating too much, or to avoid foods you like but which do you harm, is to pause for a few minutes. Measure those minutes if that makes it easier. For instance you can make a decision that you will only have another slab of chocolate or glass of beer after you have drunk some water to clear your palette.

It goes without saying that a wise choice of nourishing foods is highly desirable for children's growth and development. Adequate breakfasts before the day begins will help children's concentration levels. If their blood sugar levels drop dramatically, they are likely to be inattentive at school, even falling asleep.

Eating

It is very important to take enough time to eat and digest food. How you eat is important too. Taste your food as you chew it. Enjoy the process, rather than being distracted and mentally absent. Allow your jaw to drop down freely to receive food and to make the movements of chewing, rather than lifting the skull off the lower jaw, making all the movement with your head. Chew enough. When I was a child, the current wisdom was to chew thirty two times, once for every tooth.

You probably have already decided which meals you will take as a family and have established your expectations of table manners, and which meals you allow in front of the television. Eating is a sociable experience and in many countries is a time when the family gather together and re-establish their bonds.

Rhythm

I place much faith in the value of living rhythmically. It seems to me that human beings respond naturally to rhythm and that bodily processes are steadied and maintained by rhythm. Our heartbeat is rhythmic, the movement of the gut is rhythmic, breathing is rhythmic, and our brains pulse at differing frequencies depending on our activity level.

Rhythmic activities such as walking, running, dancing and playing music, regularise the body and keep it healthy. Try to live rhythmically and at a steady pace. Encourage your children in rhythmic activity, whether you do this at home, or take them to music, dance or exercise classes. They will develop rhythmic movement as opposed to jerky sudden movement. This is particularly good for babies and young children, but you never grow too old for rhythm.

Play

'Play is not wasted time but rather time spent building new knowledge from previous experience' [39]

Some of my pupils are surprised at the idea that they should play. They come to me imbued with a serious attitude. They have come to Learn. It is a new idea that they learn best if they adopt a playful attitude. *'Play is a powerful mediator for learning throughout a person's life'* [40]

All animals play, and they learn their skills through play. To our eyes this play can involve cruelty: batting down a captured bird when it attempts to fly away, but not to the cat that caught the bird. It acts instinctively, its paw shoots out and the bird is caught, it acts out of instinctive playfulness.

Children are naturally playful. They love to build and create a fantasy world from lego and other constructive toys. They need very simple tools: a tablecloth, some sticks, a few pots and containers to aid their imaginations and create inter-relationships. The notion of 'serious play' has been given more attention recently by psychologists and educators.

The idea of play in our culture tends to be dismissed and forgotten, except by those who have studied the most recent research into the psychology of learning. Lloyd Rieber of the University of Georgia Department of Instructional Technology, says *'Play offers a means for understanding motivation and learning in a holistic way. Serious play is not easy to achieve, but the reward is an intense and satisfying experience for both students and teachers'*. This kind of learning is rare in schools, and adults can be so conditioned by their own school experience that they expect schools to offer an environment *'where learning is regimented, homogeneous, and based more on rewards and threats than curiosity and interest'*. But Einstein clearly understood this when he wrote, *'to stimulate creativity, one must develop the childlike inclination for play.'*

In my view, play helps us maintain lightness of spirit. You are more likely to maintain lightness of body if you have lightness of spirit.

Joy

Lightness of spirit leads to living joyfully. If you are to live joyfully you will accept that you are where you are. What has happened has happened. The next thing is to notice what is happening around you. What do you observe? Do you need to take any action, or can you leave the situation to unfold? Are you poised and ready should your action be required?

When you are poised, you will be ready to adapt quickly to changing situations. Instead of constantly being in a reactive state, fighting a rear guard action, being behind the beat, you can be in a proactive state and have the freedom to choose your direction. It all depends on keeping your poise: in Alexander language, 'keeping your length'.

You will discover who you really are, not who you think you should be in relation to others. You will be able to know yourself, discover what you are passionate about and pursue it. You will give and get, rather than giving up and getting through.

11. Conclusion

'It is our choices, Harry, that show us what we truly are, far more than our abilities.' JK Rowling, Harry Potter and the Chamber of Secrets

As you begin to explore the principles of the Alexander Technique, their effect will begin to seep into your life in a full and positive way. This anchor can be relied upon in the art of living. You or your child may have come to the teaching here for one reason, such as to improve posture, but then you'll begin to realise that there are benefits in all areas of life. By playing with posture in the Alexander way you will be giving yourself and your child a solid basis for a way to live the whole of life.

The principles remind us, time and time again, that we cannot control stressful events that happen to us. We can, however, learn to control our reaction to them. As the tools of the Alexander Technique become a part of you, you will develop a deeper awareness of how stress is affecting you, and a new way to deal with the effects that stress has upon you.

Whereas you might previously have found yourself angry or upset in a flash, the gap between stimulus and response gradually widens, and you will find that you have a choice as to whether to hold your breath, grit your teeth with tension and shout or cry out – in that very moment. You now have an alternative; you can direct your neck to be free, your head to release off the top of your spine, your whole back to lengthen and widen. You can remind yourself to breathe – and let go of the grip that you have on your ribcage. Or, physical habits, developed from childhood by perhaps copying Dad's style of digging in the garden and which now cause back pain, can be re-educated to help you move as nature intended.

By stopping, thinking and acting; by taking time to do the Alexander lying down daily to reset and restore, you can gradually lower the level of habitual stress and emotional tension that you are bringing with you in every situation in your life. It is not that you won't feel emotion, but you will do so with awareness and choice.

Through your learning of the Alexander Technique you realise increasingly that you are a role model for your children whilst at the same time you are both 'stressors' to them and they are stressors to you! You love them and want the best for them, but no-one gave you an instruction manual when you had children, nor, for that matter, an instruction manual for life itself! The Alexander Technique can help you go into the future increasingly pain free, resilient and hopeful. The great variety of games provide you with fun ways to play with posture and develop Alexander thinking and skills.

Just as you cannot learn to play the violin from a book, you cannot learn all about the Alexander Technique from this book, although I hope that it has offered you some useful ideas, food for thought and games to play. If your curiosity has been awakened then you might enjoy having Alexander Technique lessons for yourself and your children to deepen your understanding and experience.

I remember one parent, the mother of two sets of twins, who found herself able to stay calmer in the midst of the inevitable mayhem and was able to prevent her anger from rising to those previous high levels where she shouted at the children and experienced most situations spiralling out of control.

Others have found themselves gradually more able to deal with what previously would have been challenging discussions with their teenager or partner. They are now more able to choose what to say and when and how to say it. Perhaps they have become more mindful of their own and the others reactions. The same goes for interactions and meetings at work. The lynchpin of being able to Stop gives one the power and freedom of choice: not to react as one would have done previously, rather to say or do something different or indeed – not to say or do anything at that moment at all, and give oneself longer to reflect on the whole situation.

Stressful school days; the changes of puberty; separated parents and additional half siblings; other family tensions – and possibly physical back shoulder or arm pain – can all contribute to a child's difficulties.

Learning the Alexander Technique can, just as for their parents, become an anchor for them, helping them to find and accept themselves as they are, and experience a calm place within themselves even though there is so much that they can't control. Gradually they can feel stronger, more able to deal with situations, to breathe and open up. They may feel more able to ask a parent or a teacher for help. Gradually as they begin to know and accept themselves for who they are, they may acquire more confidence in themselves and won't feel that they have to follow the crowd all the time. Gradually, they can learn to deal with and prevent their physical pain. Gradually, gradually ... as they become more co-ordinated and posture improves they will get more fun from sport and exercise, getting fitter and healthier, expressing themselves through music and art, feeling better about themselves, exploring life more fully and discovering what they enjoy and who they really are.

Always remember: Stop, Think, Act – stick to process in order to live joyfully.

Appendix 1: Games to play with children

'I found that if you can get a child to move around freely you can help it in many ways to become more sociable, a happier, and altogether freer child than if you just let it sit playing or being taught ...' Grethe Laub[41]

Most of the following games can be played in the family or at parties. When you lead, your child will copy. Then change round and you copy the ideas your child has. Be creative.

You need to keep the Alexander concepts in mind as you play these games and gently remind the child about keeping their length and width as you both get into them. Aim to match the game to the age, maturity and interests of your child. Keep the tone light, fun and playful.

You and your child will be familiar with some of these games or some may seem simple, however you need to approach them afresh and play them with the Alexander principles in mind.

Games Index

Energy games

The energy game is an 'awareness' game which needs to be introduced by explaining to the child that our bodies exist by having energy going through them. We become conscious of that inner energy when we are excitable, quiet, or when we get stuck in it. This may make us not feel very well and we might get a headache or tummy ache. Some people get tired very quickly and need to lie down and rest: this tonifies their energy. But not everyone likes to lie down as they can't stay still for long enough and they prefer to go for a run or do something quite vigorous in order to disperse their energy.

Tonifying and dispersing

Some people have very strong vigorous energy and can't stay still easily, getting very restless when they lie down. If their energy gets stuck you can suggest the following exercise to help release it.

The child holds a rolling pin (or any implement about a foot long with rounded ends) horizontally between his open palms which are at elbow height. He rotates his hands so that a twizzling movement is made with the pin. It is like bicycling with the hands clasping the outside of the pedals and moving them round: first one goes forward and down while the other comes back and up and the vice versa. The hands make circular movements so that one end of the rolling pin goes forward before the other end. The movement can get faster and faster, it is an excellent way of dispersing energy which has become stuck, not only for children but also for the elderly.

This game allows for larger movements, than for instance in writing, so helps free up the arms and hands. You could also do this while leaning your back against a wall as this would help you to keep your length. It can be used as a preparation for juggling as it is a guide on how to move the hands in a proper way.

Juggling

Juggling is an activity which disperses energy and keeps the child relatively still, well balanced and poised, with lively eyes. When you juggle, you need to learn first about throwing accurately. Everyone gets caught up trying to catch the juggling balls. They become so anxious about catching that they forget that the ball must land where they want it to be – in their open hand: First, throw the balls up to eye height and just let them fall to the ground. They should land just in front of your feet. There are books that describe how to learn to juggle.[42] The art starts with throwing. You have to think about throwing rather than catching and if the ball does not land in your hand you let it fall to the floor.

Juggling is not an easy skill to learn but the learning process if carried out with Alexander thinking is fun and leads to success. Not easy but worthwhile!

The water fountain – an inner energy game

The game is for one child, who has to imagine the energy flows in his body coming up from his feet like a water fountain. It is best described to the child by saying 'think of a flow of energy running all through you, coming up your legs and into your tummy and filling up; coming into your heart and filling up; under your shoulders and filling up then down your arms and running out of your fingers; up through your neck, into your head and out of the top of your head. What does it make you feel like doing when that happens?' You can suggest that the child uses his fingers to create an energy water jet, which he directs at someone to tickle them with it. He can ask if they are ticklish when he points it at their tummy or behind their knee, or calm when he puts his hand close to their back. What do they feel when he puts his hand above their head? Is it heavy? Do they feel as if his energy is bringing them up when he lifts his hand and imagines the water coming on up?

Energy cushion

Children can also experiment to see if they can feel each other's energy by putting up their palms together, about an inch apart, with a little cushion of energy between them. Ask them how it feels; is it warm, does it tingle or tickle? Experiments with energy are very successful with children because they are more sensitive to it than adults.

Refuelling

A development of this game can be tried when a child is tired and lacks energy. The adult can pretend to feel for the energy leak and heal it with his finger. He can ask where the leak is and stop it by putting an imaginary energy plaster over it and the child may even feel that his energy has returned. Roles can be reversed and a child can pretend to heal an adult.

Up and down games

These introduce the ideas of expansion and stopping in order to be more poised.

The children can run and then be told to change direction, or run and then change to jumping or moving around on tiptoes etc. They can also run with bean-bags on their heads.

If they get into pairs then one child can twizzle the second, first one way then the other, like ballerinas on their toes. The twizzling can be done with the arms up above the head or stretched out sideways. Throughout, the emphasis should be on getting the children to stop and start the twizzling while staying in balance.

Walking fingers up the wall

This game and the one after it can be taken in sequence. They help children to make the most of their height without being told to 'stand up straight'. It's important that you remind the child to keep their breathing easy and regular and to think of avoiding squeezing the back in – keeping the back wide – as their hands go up.

Ask the child to face the wall and stand with toes a few centimetres away. Raise hands so that finger tips are at elbow height and walk the fingertips, index and second fingers alternately, up the wall, until the arms are reaching tall above the head. Walk the fingers a little further up, as if you can't quite reach something you want and let yourself go onto your toes. Keep breathing! Can you reach up any further? Now let your heels drop gently onto the floor without losing contact with the place the fingertips have reached. Keep breathing all the time.

Now, keeping your hands in contact with the wall, open your arms out to the side as if they are dropping down like the handles of a corkscrew – as they come down, the cork goes up – pretend you are the cork. Have you grown any longer and taller?

Walking backwards

Now start to walk backwards, bending your knee and feeling for the ground behind you with your toe before stepping back. Turn down the room, still walking backwards, and, keeping your breathing wide and spacious, your head tall and light, and walk all the way to the wall behind you before walking forwards again, without changing your new style – wide, spacious and light.

Funny walks

When applied to a group, ask the children to get into pairs. The game is to copy the example of your partner's chosen funny walk. The child demonstrating can choose a walk that imitates someone from fantasy or real life. The character of the chosen person will show in the walk, so proud and stiff, or sad and droopy, injured or active, gymnast or ice skater, old or young, fit or unfit. See how well you can demonstrate the walk and how well you can copy it. In threes one child can watch the other two and then show how they would improve it themselves. They will become inventive and playful. For young children, animals can be the example: how a bunny rabbit hops, how a hippopotamus walks, how a lizard moves or a frog leaps.

For the older child, to raise awareness of the habits that everyone acquires, taking this for normal, they can attempt to copy the walk that they see in front of them among their friends and schoolmates. It stimulates enquiry into what they otherwise would take for granted. How does one walk in a flatfooted way, or as a springy sports player? 'How is that different from what I think is normal?'

Awareness games

Bony landmarks

For very young children:

Show me where the window is. Where's the door? Where's the floor? Where's the sky? Show me with your finger where Mummy is. Can you point your finger towards Mummy? Point your finger to the table (to the telly … the stairs … etc) Where are your feet? Where are your toes? Where are they pointing now? Point them to the window/door/

telly/etc. Point your knees to the stairs/sofa/table etc. Point your elbow to the book/shelf/mug etc, the other elbow/shoulder/ear/nose/chin/ bottom etc.

Finish with the top of the head pointing towards the ceiling and imagine it's floating up and up towards the sky. Then use this reminder when you see them in a slump: bottom down onto the chair, head up towards the ceiling.

Walking with eyes shut

This game enhances the awareness of sounds, light, smell and very light touch. The child becomes aware of his feet on the floor, his breathing and the proximity of other people. It is played by the child walking slowly and carefully around a room or garden with his eyes shut – he is not guided by anyone. He keeps himself safe because he has to think of feeling before he bumps into things. He has to think about where things are. Relaxation is important as sensitivity increases whereas fear makes us stiff and clumsy. He also listens for sounds and thinks about where they are. With our eyes shut we all become more sensitive. For instance, when walking near a window, the light on the eyelids becomes much greater and conversely it becomes darker when we turn away.

The game is particularly good when several children play it at the same time and avoid bumping into each other. Initially they might have their hands out in front of them but, as they become more confident, they can just sense when someone is close and stop in time.

A development of this game is to place soft objects (like cushions, coats, rolled up rugs) as obstacles on the floor so that the children have to stop when their feet touch them. This develops awareness in their feet.

Leading and following

This is suitable for children of all ages, with varying degrees of subtlety. The first version is played in pairs and the second can be played in threes.

In pairs, one person offers the back of his hand to a second, who closes his eyes. The first is in charge of the second and promises not to harm him, lead him into danger or frighten him. The second person trusts the first implicitly and, with eyes closed, is led wherever the first person chooses to go. The game can be progressed by making the signals more and more subtle, by not pulling so hard and by not stopping so suddenly. The aim is to balance thought and action by gradually refining the action until only thought is necessary. The leader ends up thinking he is going somewhere else and his hand makes an involuntary movement to which the second person responds. If a child is the leader and plays with an adult, then a sense of responsibility can be developed as the child is taking care of the adult. The game develops the idea of thinking rather than doing.

In threes, the child in the middle is blindfolded (you will need to find a scarf for the blindfold) and puts his right hand on to the back of one partner's left hand and his left hand on the back of the other person's right hand. The game is for the other children to lead the middle person, without speaking, and to avoid bumping into other people or things in the room. The child in the middle needs to trust his partners and have loose arms and wrists. The game can be developed into being more adventurous by walking faster, more slowly, backwards, round in circles, bending down and going under things and perhaps even going up stairs. Gradually the child should become more flexible and trusting.

Feet against feet

For this game, the children take their shoes off and sit on the floor in pairs facing each other, with their knees tucked up under their chins and as close together as possible. They then lie down on their backs and put their feet against their partner's feet and start to make circles as if bicycling with their feet. The feet must remain in contact throughout and they can experiment with movements in other directions and see who does the leading. Throughout, you should ask them to check what is happening to their backs, their breathing and their arms and remind them to 'keep their length'. It's better to organise this activity when the children are quite quiet and then do it for only a short period of time.

Palm to palm

A development of the previous game is: the children put the palms of their hands on their partner's and follow movement with their hands. Who is doing the steering? Even more sensitivity is required if they then put their fingertips together instead, or even just one fingertip, while having their eyes closed.

Back to back

The children sit together, back to back, astride a bench or chair and rock gently to and fro, feeling, moving, leading and following with their backs. This can be developed by humming at the same time, so that each child feels the buzz and hum in his back. This game is wonderfully enlivening and soothing, particularly if many pairs rock and hum together. The sound resonates through all the participants' backs and throughout the room.

Drawing in space

This involves drawing in the air with someone else's hand. The method is for one child to take hold of your hand or another child's hand or finger and to make shapes in the air with it. The aim is that the child whose hand is being moved should be free and not rigid with tension, so that the movement can be achieved without undue force. The child activating the hand needs to be clear about where the shapes are going to be drawn. The game is progressive because it can become more and more subtle. An extra element can be introduced by trying to recognise and guess the shapes being drawn. The shapes should be simple and easily identified such as animals, letters and numbers.

Drawing on someone's back

A variation of the game above is drawing a simple shape, or writing a letter of the alphabet on someone else's back and they have to guess what it is from the feel of the finger's movement. The game can be developed and made more subtle by either reducing the size of the shape or by not pressing so hard. Or it can be made more difficult by writing short words.

Drawing from the sense of touch

For this game the children are given a sheet of paper and a pencil. They sit with their eyes closed and are given an interestingly shaped object to hold, something like an orange, a banana or a key. They have to make a drawing from the feel of the object and this helps to develop spatial perception. They need to touch it without grabbing and be like cling film around it, in order to feel it better.

Throughout the game the leader can direct them about holding the pencil correctly and can also suggest that they smile across the shoulders and across the hips as they do the various activities and 'keep their length'.

Drawing with eyes closed

For this game your child needs a sheet of paper and a pencil. Suggest simple things for him to draw, with his eyes shut: things like a circle, a square, a tree and a house. Then look at the strange drawings together. This develops kinaesthetic awareness, the sense of knowing what the body is doing even with your eyes closed. Are you doing what you think you are doing?

You can ask your child to describe to you with words how you should draw a house, tree, apple or box. Use these instructions to send your pencil around the contours of the object. Try this with your eyes open, closed, and then with both players' eyes closed or try exchanging roles.

Drawing your feelings

This can be played in two ways. The first involves drawing or writing on a piece of paper. If you draw or write when feeling cross, then the pencil makes a deep mark on the paper and the appearance of the writing is heavier, more abrupt, jagged and fierce. In contrast, when you allow the pencil tip to tell you where it is going, your shoulders become less bossy and you have more sensitivity in your fingers and this opens up your feelings. The aim of the game is for the child to make the pencil behave according to the way he is feeling. He decides what he wants to draw and, while doing it, he experiments with different feelings such as sadness, excitement, joy, depression or anger. He sees how the pencil reacts and the kind of picture which results.

Alternatively one could suggest a simple thing for him to draw five times on a single sheet of paper. The first time he could draw it in an angry mood, then in a frightened state, followed by a happy mood, a sleepy mood and finally in a calm and peaceful mood. You then look at all the drawings and see if they appear different.

When someone touches you it is often possible to tell how they are feeling. Are they feeling positive, negative, loose, tight, heavy or light? The second version of the game is to try and detect these feelings in another person. The children play it in pairs and one child touches the other on his shoulder and, while doing so, he has to imagine different feelings such as being very tense, very cross, very happy, very sleepy or very calm. The second child has to guess what he is feeling as the nature of the touching should reflect it. The only drawback to the game is that some children may fib about their feelings, but that could lead into a different game!

Handling mystery objects

There are several ways of playing this game. The teacher has a selection of objects such as a fir cone, a rubber, a marble and a range of everyday household items which she keeps hidden in a bag. The children sit in a circle, with their eyes closed, and an object is passed from one to the other; when it has gone all round the circle, they put up their hands if they think they know what it is and one of them is chosen to say. The game continues in the same way. Alternatively, the children take it in turns to close their eyes and try to guess what the object is, while the others watch. A third way is for the children to get into pairs. Each couple is given a lucky dip bag containing a few objects and they take it in turns to close their eyes and guess what each object is. All of these games develop sensitivity of touch and perception.

Where's your tongue?

Sometimes we get very tense when we are thinking a lot. Also when we are feeling things, our faces can reflect this; they can look grumpy or happy but sometimes we hold the look right inside the face and it makes us feel quite tight and tense. A good way of recognising if we have this habit of holding our faces very stiffly is to ask ourselves the question 'Where's your tongue? Is it in the roof of the mouth? Is it on the bottom or is it curled up?' A parent could also ask a child these surprise questions when walking along the street or when watching television. With role reversal a child might ask an adult the same questions when they are preparing the meal or reading the paper.

A variation on this game is to say 'freeze your tongue and notice where it is'. Is it pushing against the roof of your mouth, are you pressing it against your teeth or are you curling it back? Suggest the child does things with his tongue. Ask him how far he can curl it backwards in his mouth. Suggest that he curls it down, behind the lower teeth and tries to feel the bit of skin right underneath the tongue. Get him to stick his tongue right out as far as it will go and ask if he can touch his nose, his chin or his cheek.

Ask the child to notice what happens to his tongue when he talks and makes different sounds. What happens when he says a word like Timbuktu or tries to say a tongue twister like 'Peter Piper picked a peck of pickled pepper' or 'red lorry, yellow lorry'? Ask him to think of some other tongue twisters and see how fast he can say them.

Calming strategies

Lying down with eyes closed

Lie down with the children in the Alexander 'Reset and Restore' position first. When everyone is quiet, with their eyes closed then explore ideas of opening up internally.

During this time you can direct the feeling inside the children so that they become more expanded and restful. They need to become like a calm, still pool, spreading out and smiling across the hips, shoulders and in the face. You could ask 'Where is your tongue?' at this point. You can direct their faces to relax and bring their attention to deep behind the eyes and get them to imagine a big space inside the head in between the ears. You can also direct them to open the throat and have a big space inside.

Going inside

This game is about balancing the energies of the body while they are lying down on their backs. You can explain how the energy gets buzzy when people are excited and how it becomes quiet when people are calmer. Whilst the children are lying down quietly, you can get them to feel the breathing through the nose and notice how it is moving the rib cage and tummy. Notice any buzzing feelings in the hands feet and legs, which come from being busy and alive.

You can then direct the children's attention to going deeper inside themselves and forgetting the outside world; to close their eyes, stop looking, and instead think of the big space inside their bodies.

You can then bring them back into contact with the world outside by getting in touch with their sensations of hands, feet, and breathing and then becoming aware of sounds in the room. They can open their eyes and see what's around them, notice colours and movement and begin to be aware of subtleties that they haven't noticed before. Are the edges of objects the same colour? What happens to colour in the corners of the room? If the sun is shining, what happens to the shadows? Are they moving? What sounds are there, how quiet, loud, far away, near? What can they smell?

This game expands their awareness to be aware of themselves and of the outside world at the same time.

The pre-meal game

The whole family can play this game. It is an excellent way of calming and quietening children before having a meal. When the children get to the table they should sit down with their feet touching the ground, close their eyes, and stay still and silent for a whole minute. The idea is to listen and count the number of different noises they can hear. There will be background noises like the wind, the rain, the ticking of the clock and the sound of traffic going past. There may also be noises in the room like an occasional cough or sniffle, or the cat purring or scratching. When the minute is up everyone says how many noises they heard and then they start the meal in a calm and peaceful way.

One minute of silence

We all live such rushed and hectic lives nowadays that moments of calm are rare. A way of helping children to experience a moment of calm is to build it into their daily routine. This will help them to become more organised. A good way to do this is to sit quietly in the car for a minute before going off to school in the morning. During this period of silence everyone should try not to think of anything in particular, in order that things will come to mind, like the packed lunch left on the kitchen table or the library books which need to be returned that day. You can use this at any time of day or in any situation or location to calm things down.

Humming

Humming is to develop listening and can be played by two children, a group of children or by a family as a 'Game of Preparation'. Even people who are not particularly musical can listen to sound. If two people make a continuous noise and, at the same time, slowly move their voices up and down like a siren, it is possible to hear what happens to the sound when the voices nearly meet and almost throb. If two children hum in different ways and let their voices roam around, up and down, then they can hear how the sounds mingle with each other.

The game can have a very calming effect if it is played by a family before a meal. Each member of the family chooses a note to hum and holds it for as long as the breath lasts. They can then choose a different note to hum when they take a new breath. Everyone should notice what the sound is like. Does it make the room resonate? Does it make the glasses on the table vibrate or tingle? Does it make you buzz? The game could also be played in the car before starting a journey. How does the sound compare? Is it different again when played in the bedroom before going to sleep?

Stop and go games

Dead fishes

This is a group game for stillness and it involves the children lying down and pretending to be dead fishes. Anyone who moves is called out and the last person to remain still is the winner.

The Dead fishes game can also be played to music with the children lying down, making movements until the music stops when they should stay still.

Musical Statues & Musical Chairs

In the traditional games of 'Musical Statues' and 'Musical Chairs' children are again able to practice changing between movement and stillness. In 'Musical Statues' the children run or jump around the room and then stay completely still when the music stops. In 'Musical Chairs' the children run or jump around the room and then have to quickly find a chair and sit down when the music stops. Alternatively, you could be creative and devise a form of musical chairs which involves more balancing or more stillness than usual.

Grandmother's footsteps

This familiar game is played by the children spreading out at the far end of the room from the one who is chosen to be grandmother. 'Grandmother' stands with back turned to the others who have to race to be the first to touch her. However no-one must be seen moving when 'grandmother' turns round which she does unexpectedly. Anyone seen moving must retire to the starting point.

Simon says

This is a game which most children know and is good for teaching 'stopping' and 'going'. Every time the leader says 'Simon says do something', (such as sit down, stand up, laugh, jump etc) the children have to do it but if she only says 'do this', then they must not respond. They can easily be caught out!

Decision-making

The 'deciding game' has the object of improving a child's decision-making powers. The method of playing the game is to ask very simple questions that involve the child making a decision. Questions like 'Where shall I put this book? How high shall I reach? How many steps shall I take to cross the room?' The child should be encouraged to make a decision without hesitating too much. It is a good game for trying to eradicate a child's fear of making the wrong decision.

The driving game

This 'decision-making' and 'will power' game is one where children are given power over their parent in the car. There needs to be a very strict rule about your right to veto anything which you think is unsuitable. A good time to play this game is on the journey home from school. The children take it in turns to direct the driver. They give instructions such as turn left, turn right or go straight on as each junction is approached, allowing plenty of time for the driver to signal. It gives young children a good mental map of the location of where they live. The parent can always say if she considers it unsuitable, but the occasional foray into a dead-end road can be quite good fun. Children enjoy the game because it is an adventure; they can lead the parent astray and get themselves into tight corners or even lost. They can discover new places which they didn't know existed. Ultimately if it goes on too long and the parent feels bored or tired, she can say that they have to get home and from now on she will only obey instructions which take them in that direction

Balancing games

Small children are always testing their balance by walking on walls or balancing themselves in other ways. Here are some variations to introduce. Objects can be balanced on any part of the body, so the game is for the child to balance things in strange positions. He could try balancing a bean bag on his elbow, a ball on his knee or a tall stick on his hand. Alternatively, the child can try balancing himself on an unstable object like a gym ball.

Another variation is for the adult to kneel down and support the child standing and balancing on the adult's folded knees. The adult could sit in a chair and support the child balancing on his knees in that position. The game can be made more difficult by combining the two activities of balancing an object whilst being in a funny position.

The Alexander Technique is all about poised and balanced movement. So we want to stay relaxed and calm, rather than tensing to hold our balance.

Imitating animals

Animal movement is copied mostly on all fours, though monkeys, bears, and kangaroos are among the animals who can balance on two legs as well. The animal might sidle crossways as horses are sometimes trained to do, or jump sideways like a cat does when playing with something. The children could also be tortoises, firstly with heads in their shells and then with them out or monkeys in a half-upright position. There are many animals which can be imitated. These games should be accompanied by the leader talking about making space to move in, which introduces the idea of where the children are going, in other words, the idea of direction.

An additional element can be added by asking one child to move like an animal of their choice and the other children have to guess which animal is being represented.

Walking tall game

The child or children imagine that they are a person carrying a pot of water from a well or river or some books on their head. They have to imagine that it is very heavy and they are balancing it on their heads and thinking about how they would walk. Maybe some props could be used, like a bean bag or cushion to put on their heads. Or they could imagine they are jugglers with twizzling sticks with a plate on top.

Balance boards and rocker boards

Rocker boards are pieces of wood about 30cm square fitted with two rockers underneath. One can balance on them with the rockers placed either front to back or side to side. The game is to stand on it and not let the edge of the board touch the ground. The aim is for it to move freely rather than being fixed by stiff legs in a still position.

A balance board is a piece of plywood about two and a half feet long and one foot wide, with a roller underneath and a stop at either end to prevent the roller slipping out. The child stands on the board, with one foot at each end, and as the roller is in between, it rolls to and fro so that the board see-saws. It is quite difficult to stay balanced and children enjoy the challenge. Stay close for a while to avert any accidents. The child should find it easier to balance if he looks forward and out, rather than at his feet. These games are great for improving balance in any activity.

Rhythm

Rhythm can be developed by saying things in certain ways. Whole sentences can be said in a rhythm, things like 'have a very nice day', 'put your coat on' and 'whoops I dropped it'. Also names can be said in a rhythm – Melanie – Jonathan – Sebastian – Angelina. Children can also be encouraged to clap the sentences and names.

Rhythm can also be developed by any singing of songs and nursery rhymes and, for more musical children, the singing of rounds such as 'London's burning' and 'Three blind mice' is excellent. Even children without a musical ear have an excellent sense of rhythm and can benefit from oral training.

Knowing your body games

The Grand Old Duke of York

This is suitable for young children aged 4 to 6 years. The leader asks the children if they know the song and she stomps around the room singing it, with the children joining in and following in a line behind. After a while, she asks them what actions they could put to the song and they experiment together with the children's suggestions, one by one. She then tells them that she has some different ideas and would like them to copy her. The first time it could be done on the spot by standing up straight (for when they were up they were up), going into a squat position (for when they were down they were down) and into a half-way bending position (for when they were only half way up). It could then be repeated by walking, jumping or marching in each of the three positions. The children should be reminded to keep their length and not pull their heads back in whatever position they find themselves. These movements become quite difficult but are great fun to try and the children will love the ensuing mayhem.

The game can progress even further by introducing additional actions at the same time, such as hands stretched up above the head or out to the side, or by doing things in a slow way, sad way or in a fast happy way. The leader should encourage the children to have their own ideas and everyone will enjoy the antics which result.

Parcel drama describing game

This is a group game for older children who try to get someone who is lying still on the floor to respond to their detailed instructions, merely by means of description rather than with direct commands like 'stand up'. The children have to organise their language in such a way as to describe what they want him to do, for example 'roll over onto your left side, then put the palm of your right hand on the floor, then push up on this hand etc. It is extremely difficult to explain exactly what you want someone to do and to direct them through an action like standing up. The instructions can be easily misunderstood and the whole game can be very funny.

Doing too much

This one enables the children to explore the concepts of too much effort, too little effort and just the right amount of effort. The children walk around the room shaking each other's hand and greeting everyone by name. Firstly they do it with too much effort, having their hands too big and strong, then with too little effort, with their hands too soft and weak and finally with their hands just right. For young children under the age of about seven, the leader could tell them the story of Goldilocks and the three bears at the same time, varying the story to reflect too much, too little and just the right effort.

In the home this can be introduced as part of normal play or story telling.

Startle pattern

This is a game for learning about what goes wrong. Children can grow up thinking that everything has to be done correctly and they can get worried if they do something wrong. It is important for them to be able to do things wrongly and to make a point of observing how grossly wrong they are. When anyone is startled they go into special positions and this can be illustrated in a game situation. The leader should devise a game where she makes a sudden noise, perhaps with a loud rattle or by banging on a tin with a hammer, and the children have to go into positions where they show their reactions to being frightened. The best way is for the leader to make up a scary story and build it up to a crescendo and make the bang. Perhaps something like 'One night it is very dark and you are walking around the house and hear a sudden noise'. The children should go into their startle pattern and freeze so that they can look at each other and see what funny positions they are all in. The story should then continue with plenty of opportunities for showing scared reactions and positions of protection against danger.

A variation on this game is for everyone to sit down on the floor in a circle and for the leader to talk about what goes wrong. She could describe an incident and then get the children to join in and suggest what happens. Something like: 'The other day I was in my car and I noticed that someone was going to bump into the back of me. What do you think I did?' The children can talk about their ideas or act them out. This provides an opportunity for talking about reactions. The leader can then tell them what she actually did. The children can also be encouraged to talk about a time when they can remember something going really wrong and what they did. What sort of position did they get into? They could also be asked to describe their reactions to frightening things on the television.

Bossy bits

It is possible for parts of the body to respond so strongly to certain feelings that they take over and make movements happen in a funny way. Doing too much can progress into getting stuck. The leader can talk to the children and explain how bits of the body become too bossy and start to boss the rest of the body about. She can then suggest that they do some acting to demonstrate this. They can act out characters in stories that they know or ones in stories which she makes up using descriptive people like Mrs Worry, Mr Swagger, Mrs Hurry, Mr Down, Mrs Up and Miss Happy. Mr Swagger may find that his legs and feet are bossing his body about or maybe his elbow is doing it. Mrs Hurry might find that her chin is trying to get there too quickly. Miss Happy's face may be too bossy or perhaps her feet will be so tingly that they push the rest of her body about.

Getting stuck

Getting stuck is an important game which is great fun to play. Get the children to pretend that they are stuck in the mud with bees buzzing around their heads and they can't escape. Alternatively, they could pretend to be tied up by cannibals who are going to eat them. Another variation is to play a team game where each child has to pretend that its legs can only move by hopping. Arrange the children in teams and line them up on one side of the room and give each child a beanbag. Put a waste paper basket opposite each team on the other side of the room. Each team member in turn has to hop across to his or her basket and drop the beanbag in. It is a race to see which team finishes first.

Light and heavy

In this game the leader asks the children to flop over, with hands down to the floor and with everything (apart from their legs) being completely loose and limp and then they shake themselves. Now she explains to the class that she wants them all to imagine that they are inflatable toys (such as soldiers or dragons) which are being blown up very slowly. They need to imagine that they are being pumped up, bit by bit; first the air goes into their legs, then into their hips, followed by their tummies, chests, arms and finally into their heads. Their bodies should respond accordingly.

It is interesting for the leader to notice how they end up. If they are too stiff and stand holding their breath, she can suggest that they let out a little bit of the air so that the air inside them comfortably supports them. They can then think of being suspended by a golden thread and being drawn up to the sky. At the same time they should be encouraged to breathe out and, with their necks free, do some gentle nodding with their faces comfortably dropping.

A variation on the game is for the children to get in pairs and for one of them to lie down on the floor. The second child uses his hand to move his partner's floppy limbs about and then to drop them gently. While doing it the children should be asked questions like 'Who's doing the steering? Are the limbs very heavy or very light? Are they stiffening up?'Alternatively the first child could stand up and flop right over like a rag doll and his partner can move his limp limbs around.

Bones are quite heavy and to demonstrate this, the leader can suggest that the second child notices how heavy the limbs are as he lifts each arm and leg. She can then ask the child lying down to deliberately stiffen his limbs so that they become impossible to lift.

Wax works

This is a game where the children pretend to be at Madame Tussauds and become a wax work there. They can be human beings that they know, or creatures; they get into an appropriate posture which has to be held, in such a way that they feel what it is like to be that person. Another way of playing it is for the leader to tell them who she wants them to be – perhaps a character from a television programme.

Sitting bones

This needs to be introduced by showing the group a picture of a skeleton and explaining where everyone sits on their sitting bones and how their bones connect. Children can sit on their fingers and easily feel their sitting bones. They can then experiment with where they are sitting by rocking from side to side, from sitting bone to sitting bone, and allowing the skeleton to expand inside the body keeping the spine lengthening.

In all these games seeing others do something helps them develop observational powers to notice what they are doing in themselves.

Poise games

Daisy chain

One child leads the group as the head and the other children form a chain behind as the body. They hold on to each other and follow the leader's movements which can become quite complex, such as looping under the other children's arms.

Three legged race

The children get into pairs and each has one of his legs tied to his partner's. This is a particularly important game as it introduces the concepts of timing and balance; it also teaches them about co-ordination and co-operation. The children have to learn to share their balance with someone else and to get the timing right for the forward movement of the tied leg. Otherwise they fall over. Little procedures such as counting can be introduced to help them co-operate and work together. The children will need to practise for quite a while and then they can take part in a team race.

Discovering planes of movement

The children run about and punch the air in three dimensions. Then they are asked to change to movements in only two dimensions: just forwards and backwards and up and down, like Charlie Chaplin. The leader can continue by getting them to imagine that they are pieces of paper which are folded in half at the hips and ask how they would move. She can demonstrate the action too. They can then imagine the paper being folded down the other axis, so that the fold is inwards down the mid-line of the body, with the hands going towards each other. What happens when the paper is crumpled? The response to this will be a general collapse of the body. The leader then asks them to think of various parts of the body as being hinges and to see how these can change the collapse. The knee and elbow joints are hinges which can be moved and the hip joint can be used to pick the leg up and swing it. These movements at the hinges result in the body becoming puppet-like and this leads into a directed game of being puppets with actions like walking, sitting and lifting the arms and legs.

A progression of this game is for the children to pretend to be animals on the ground; creatures like caterpillars, lizards and worms. When moving flat on the ground it is the head which leads and the body follows, but it is necessary for the children to know where they are going and for them to choose the direction and also to be able to change it. When they have experimented with these movements for a while, the leader can suggest that they race each other across the room. This can be followed by imitating animals on their hind legs. When dogs or cats get on to their hind legs, they become more wobbly and the children can experiment with this.

Throughout these games you should be instructing the children to be thinking about going up, leaving the neck free and keeping their length, and to imagine spreading their webbed feet or alternatively, remaining springy.

Appendix 2: Scientific Support

'When an investigation comes to be made, it will be found that every single thing we are doing in the work is exactly what is being done in Nature, where the conditions are right, the difference being that we are learning to do it consciously' FM Alexander

From the earliest days of Alexander's work, people have been interested in increasing their understanding of the mechanisms involved and the potential of the Alexander Technique in health and education. In 1937, nineteen doctors all of whom had practical experience of Alexander's work collectively petitioned the British Medical Association for the inclusion of the Alexander Technique in the medical curriculum.

Alexander's discoveries have been supported by scientific and medical opinion since the 1930s. A survey of investigations into the Technique show anecdotal evidence that posture was improved with lessons in the Technique; performance was enhanced, lung capacity was significantly improved, and the Technique was rated by patients as the best of thirteen activities introduced for pain management.[43]

Nikolaas Tinbergen, Nobel prize winner for Physiology or Medicine in 1973, expounded upon the benefits of the Alexander Technique and the need for further scientific investigation. In 2008, a randomised control trial led by Professor Paul Little of Southampton University into non-specific chronic back pain (ATEAM trial) was published in the British Medical Journal.[44] 24 lessons in the Alexander Technique proved most beneficial both in terms of reducing pain and increasing normal functioning in daily life. Interestingly, 6 lessons followed by an exercise prescription proved to be 70% as effective.

There is evidence that lessons in the Alexander Technique are likely to lead to sustained benefit for people with Parkinson's disease.[45]

Findings by Dr Tim Cacciatore in 2011 indicate the Alexander Technique changes how anti-gravity muscle tension is regulated and that it reduces stiffness along the spine and hips.[46] It suggests that the Alexander Technique stand-to-sit movement improves both postural tone and general co-ordination. Alexander Technique teachers involved in the study were able to achieve a smoother, more continuous movement than the control subjects, consistent with previous claims that the Alexander Technique teaches more efficient movement.

While considering improvements in performance the following experiences of two athletes are noteworthy. Paul Collins, Canadian National Marathon Champion 1949–52 and veteran world record holder in 10 events, has said: *'Through the Alexander Technique I was able to rehabilitate my running after 25 years of being unable to run through injuries, to the extent that I was able to set ten world records for veterans in 1982.'*[47]

Howard Payne, Commonwealth record hammer thrower, improved his throw by 5.64 metres at the age of 37. Commenting on this improvement, which he believed was due primarily to taking Alexander lessons, he stated: *'Balance is a vital aspect of good hammer throwing and getting the head, neck, spine and pelvis in the correct relationship enables the balance of the throw to come so much more easily. Once the balance is settled there is an enormous improvement in turning speed.'*[48]

There have been some recent studies on the effect of the Alexander Technique on music training and performing. In 2007 singers' vocal quality and pianists' evenness of touch were measured following Alexander lessons and found to have improved.[49] A study of stress conducted by M Nielson in 1994 found that the Alexander Technique was as effective as beta-blocker medications in controlling the stress response during and orchestral performance.[50] Dr Wilfred Barlow studied music students and found that after lessons, all the students improved physically, had become more psychologically balanced, were easier to teach and their success in an important competition was far greater than could have been expected.[51] In earlier studies FP Jones (1972) showed that there were measurable changes in vocal resonance indicated by spectral analysis, and Doyle (1984) showed objective improvements in violinists.[52, 53]

There are currently more studies underway including the ATLAS trial funded by Arthritis Research UK and run by the University of York looking into the effectiveness of the Alexander Technique on neck pain.

It is evident that the Alexander Technique is beginning to be taken seriously in scientific and medical circles. Although research into the Technique is not yet widely established, these preliminary finding are showing encouraging results.

Acknowledgements

I don't know where to start with my thanks. In fact, I have had so much help over the forty year gestation of this book that I really consider that my peers have written it all themselves! I feel I have only been instrumental in bringing the wisdom of others to the public view. My thanks go to Jean Clark, my first and honoured Alexander Technique teacher and long term close friend, who set me on this path of discovery and whose influence I carry with me daily.

Also my deep affection and thanks to my colleagues who have supported me and taken part in discussions and presentations on the subject of teaching children the Alexander Technique in an accessible and digestible form since the 1980s. In a large part, the book is in memory of Grethe Laub, that wise and humble teacher of humanity and lover of children of all ages.

I am very grateful to Oundle School music department who offered me a post as teacher of the Alexander Technique nine years ago and have been consistently encouraging and supportive. I would also like to thank the Alexander Technique teachers Jenny Walsh, Fiona Bryan, Julia Cowper, and also Angus Gibbon, at Oundle who have helped me to develop new teaching ideas.

More specifically, enormous thanks for practical help with editing and improving the text go to Malcolm Williamson and to my publishers Kamal Thapen and Claire Rennie at HITE, who have encouraged me to write. Thanks also to Miranda Fyfe for her support and proof reading skills.

The bedrock of my life, my husband, has been consistently supportive when I have been in 'author mode', and has soothed and delighted me with fine wine and good cooking.

Sue Holladay, August 2012

References

1. Hale, R.B. & Coyle, T. (1989) *Albinus on Anatomy (Dover Anatomy for Artists)*, New York, Dover
2. Reich, W. (1933) *Character Analysis*, 3rd Ed (1972) New York, Farrar, Strauss and Giroux
3. Alexander, F. M. (1910) *Man's Supreme Inheritance, 6th edition* (1996), London, UK, Mouritz
   Alexander, F. M. (1923) *Constructive Conscious Control of the Individual*, 3rd edition (2004), London, UK, Mouritz
   Alexander, F. M. (1932) *The Use of the Self*, Edition (1985), London, UK, Victor Gollancz
   Alexander, F. M. (1941) *Universal Constant in Living*, 4th Edition (2000), London, UK, Mouritz
4. James, W. (1890) *The Principles of Psychology*, (2007) New York, Cosimo
5. Goddard Blythe, S. (2009) *Attention Balance and Co-ordination—the ABC of learning success*, Kindle Edition, Wiley
6. Mayman, M. (1968) 'Early Memories and Character Structure', *Journal of Projective Techniques and Personality Assessment* Vol. 32, Iss. 4
7. Institute for the Achievement of Human Potential www.iahp.org (accessed May 2012)
8. Hannaford, C. (1995) *Smart Moves*, USA, Great Ocean Publishers
9. Conable, B. (2000) *What Every Musician Needs to Know About the Body*, Oregon, Andover Press
10. Whittaker, E. (3 June 2000) *The Little School remembered by Erica Whittaker*: An Interview with Sue Merry and Angelo Cinque, Edinburgh, AT Media Productions
11. Quoted in Merry, S. (2011) *The Little School*, http://suemerry.vpweb.co.uk/upload/The%20Little%20School%20Pamphlet.pdf originally published in The Alexander Times, Easter Term 1934

12. Quoted in Merry, S. (2011) *The Little School,* http://suemerry.vpweb.co.uk/upload/The%20Little%20School%20Pamphlet.pdf originally published in The Alexander Times, Easter Term 1934

13. Merry, S. (1999) *Primary School Children and the Alexander Technique: A guide for classroom teachers,* Kingston-upon-Thames, UK, Education 2000

14. Merry, S. & Kleinmann, J. (2009) *Edukindness: The Alexander Technique in Primary Education* [online], Available from http://www.scribd.com/doc/21503562/Edukindness-Second-Draft (accessed 14 April 2010)

15. Carrington, W. (1994) *Thinking Aloud,* San Francisco, Mornum Time Press

16. Murdoch, R. 'Born to Sing' (1996) in *Curiosity Recaptured,* ed Jerry Sontag, Amsterdam, Mornum Time Press

17. Dimon, T. (1999), *The Undivided Self,* USA, North Atlantic Books

18. Carrington, W. (1994) *Thinking Aloud,* San Francisco, Mornum Time Press

19. Ellison, P. T. (1993) *American Journal of Human Biology* Volume 5, Issue 2, pages 193–201, Wiley Periodicals

20. Helander MG, Quance LA. (1990) 'Effects of work-rest schedules-on spinal shrinkage in the sedentary worker', *Applied Ergonomics,* 21:279–284

21. Norris, C. (2000) *Back Stability,* Champaign, Illinois, Human Kinetics

22. Grenfell, J. (1976) *Requests the Pleasure,* Ed 2006 London, Hodder and Stoughton

23. Faber, A. and Mazlish, E. (1980) *How to talk so kids will listen and how to listen so kids will talk,* New York, Avon

24. Gordon Training International and Gordon Training UK www.gordontraining.com (accessed May 2012)

25. Brian Gym International www.braingym.org (accessed April 2012)

26. Carskadon et al, 'Adolescent Sleep Patterns, Circadian Timing,

and Sleepiness at a Transition to Early School Days', *SLEEP* Vol. 21, No. 8, 1998

27. Vgontzas et al, 'Elevation of Plasma Cytokines in Disorders of Excessive Daytime Sleepiness: Role of Sleep Disturbance and Obesity', *The Journal of Endocrinology and Metabolism*, Sept 2012 http://jcem.endojournals.org/content/82/5/1313.short
28. Bates, W.H. (1943) *Better Eyesight without Glasses* Ed (1977), London, Souvenir Press
29. East, A. (2012) Embody Magazine: '1,022 parents were polled by the Society of Teachers of the Alexander Technique during July 2012', London, STAT News
30. Dukette, D. and Cornish, D. (2009) *The Essential 20: Twenty Components of an Excellent Health Care Team*, Pittsburg, Rose Dog Books
31. Buzan, T. (20034) *Mind Maps For Kids: An Introduction*, London, Thorsons
32. Vinten Fenton, J. (1973) *Choice of Habit: Poise, Free Movement and the Practical Use of the Body*, London, Macdonald & Evans
33. Batson, G. 'The Alexander Technique: its role in Dance' Training www.alexandertechnique.com/articles/dance/ (accessed Feb 2012)
34. Nettl-Fiol, R. & Vanier, L. (2011) *Dance and the Alexander Technique: Exploring the Missing Link*, Chicago, University of Illinois Press
35. Bluethenthale, A. (1996) 'Before you Leap' in *Curiosity Recaptured*, ed Jerry Sontag, Amsterdam, Mornum Time Press
36. NHS Back Pain at Work http://www.nhs.uk/Livewell/workplacehealth/Pages/backpainatwork.aspx (accessed May 2012)
37. Hanefield, N. (1997) Alexander and Montessori, *The Alexander Journal* No. 15 Autumn 1997 pp27-30, London, UK, STAT Books, pp27-30
38. Simpson, A. (2008) One third of British Children Suffer Back Pain [online], *The Daily Telegraph*, Available from www.telegraph.co.uk/health/3203694/One-third-of-British-children-

suffer-back-pain.html (accessed May 2011)
Daily Mail, (16 Oct 2008) Half of British Children Suffer Back Pain Due to Slouch Potato Lifestyle [online], *Daily Mail*, http://www.dailymail.co.uk/health/article-1078072/Half-British-children-suffer-pain-slouch-potato-lifestyles.html (accessed May 2011)

39. Isenberg, J. P. & Quisenberry, N. (2002) Play: Essential for all children, *Childhood Education*, 79(1), 33-39.
40. Rieber, L. P., Smith, L., & Noah, D. (1998) The value of serious play, *Educational Technology*, 38(6), 29-37.
41. Armstrong, J. (1984) *An Alexander Teacher's View of Child-Education: An Interview with Grethe Laub*, Boston, USA, The Boston Center for the Alexander Technique
42. Cassidy, J. and Rimbeaux, B. C. (1983) *Juggling for the complete klutz*, USA, Fontana
43. Stevens, C. The Development of the Alexander Technique and Evidence for its Effects, First published in *British Journal of Therapy and Rehabilitation*, November 1997, Vol 2, No 11, p. 621-626
44. Little, P. (2008) Randomised controlled trial of alexander technique lessons, exercise and massage (ATEAM) for chronic and recurrent back pain, *BMJ* 2008; 337:a884
45. Stallibrass, C. (2002) Randomised controlled trial of the Alexander Technique for idiopathic Parkinson's disease, *Clinical Rehabilitation Journal* 16: 705-718
46. Cacciatore et al (2011) Increased dynamic regulation of postural tone through Alexander Technique training. *Human Movement Science Journal*, Feb 2011, 30(1): 74–89 and Cacciatore et al (2011) Prolonged weight-shift and altered spinal coordination during sit-to-stand in practitioners of the Alexander Technique, *Gait & Posture Journal*, June 2011, GAIPOS-3329
47. Stevens, C. (1987) *Alexander Technique - Alternative Health*, London, Optima
48. Payne, H. (1968) How I Improved this Year, *Athletics Weekly* Nov 30th 18-20

49. Williamon, A. and Coimbra, D. (2007) Proceedings of the International Symposium on Performance Science 2007, Utrecht, Netherlands, European Association of Conservatoires (AEC) pp. 369-374

50. Stevens, C. (1994) *The Alexander Technique: Medical and Physiological Aspects*, 'A Study of Stress Amongst Professional Musicians' by Nielsen M., London, STAT Books

51. Barlow, W. (1978) *More Talk of Alexander*, 'Research at the Royal College of Music', 2nd Ed. (2005) pp 204-210 London, Mouritz

52. Pierce Jones, F. (1972) Voice Production as a Function of Head Balance in Singers, *Journal of Psychology* Vol .82 pp209-215, Washington DC

53. Doyle J. (1984) *The Task of the Violinist: Skill, Stress and the Alexander Technique*, PhD thesis, University of Lancaster, England